ENDORS.

Worship God! And Praise Away the Pounds! is NOT another diet book; it is not another formula on how to lose weight! It *is* a book about listening to God speak specifically to us about food for our individual bodies. Tonya's real-life journey with deep and personal transparencies of both defeats and victories are her personal testimony on how God can bring us to a place of peace and health in our bodies. She shares not only about listening to God on what to eat, but also listening to our bodies on how what we eat makes us feel. She shares how food is our fuel for a healthy life, full of vigor and purpose! Tonya's testimony of the journey God took her on will both challenge and encourage you. You will laugh and sometimes cry as you read about her journey, but you will also walk away with incentive to make lifestyle changes in your own relationship with food and how it affects you! God grant you success as you, along with Tonya, gain new freedoms to walk in the best God intended for you!

—Lindee Hopkins
Worship Leader and Pastor's Wife
Full Faith City Church

Hebrews 12:1 (KJV) states, "Wherefore seeing we also are compassed about with so great a cloud of witnesses, let us lay aside every weight, and the sin which doth so easily beset us, and let us run with patience the race that is set before us."

Worship God! And Praise Away the Pounds! is an excellent book about how God showed Tonya what true worship and praise is and how to prepare her mind and body to praise and worship Him.

The Lord has shown Tonya that it is the "weights" in life that we have to deal with, and in her case the visible evidence was being overweight. The invisible evidence was realizing the reality of sin that we all have to deal with. Sin is a weight that is unseen, but we all carry it at one time or another.

I thank the Lord Jesus Christ for the wonderful gift He has given Tonya and for her courage and boldness to be so transparent about her life in order to help others *"Worship God! And Praise Away the Pounds!"*

—Ravon C. Rainey, Th.D.
President/Founder, Victorious Life Bible Institute

WORSHIP GOD!
AND PRAISE AWAY
THE POUNDS!

WORSHIP GOD!
AND PRAISE AWAY
THE POUNDS!

A Romans 12:1-2 Journey

TONYA WILLIAMSON

REDEMPTION
PRESS

Published by Redemption Press, PO Box 427, Enumclaw, WA 98022.

ISBN 13: 978-1-63232-619-5 (Print)
           978-1-63232-620-1 (ePub)
           978-1-63232-621-8 (Mobi)
Library of Congress Catalog Card Number: 2010913349

CONTENTS

ACKNOWLEDGMENTS

I THANK GOD for giving me the opportunity to share my life with people. I'm grateful and extremely humbled He considered me fit and worthy of such a task. I also thank God for transforming me so I am nothing like the person I used to be. Thanks to Him, I'm no longer a caterpillar, but a butterfly!

I thank my husband, Rodger, for making it possible for me to be able to stay home and write. I thank him for always being willing to work, provide, and support me in everything I desire to do.

I thank Proverbs 31 Ministries for making it possible for me to pitch my book to publishing companies. I especially thank them for being great examples of godly women who openly share their stories. You are an example to me! Thank you for doing the work of the Lord with excellence.

I thank Barbara Kois for coaching me in the beginning of this project. I thank her for her great ideas, encouragement, and boosting my confidence.

I thank Mary (I don't know her last name), one of my editors, for her helpful and positive feedback and for encouraging me to be confident.

I thank my friends who prayed for me. As I wrote this book, I went through the hardest time of my life. (I won't mention names because I don't want to miss anyone! You know who you are!)

I thank Shauna Shipman, Lindee Hopkins, and Elder Ravon Rainey, Th.D., for reading the manuscript and giving me feedback. I was so nervous! Your encouragement, approval, cheer, and support helped more than you could possibly know.

I thank the following people and ministries for having the biggest impact on my life when it comes to being examples of encouragement, service, humility, and transparency. I've listened to and learned from them for many years. Seeing how they have impacted lives for the better, including mine, has given me the courage to speak about things that made me feel embarrassed and ashamed. I thank them for always being open and honest about painful, real-life issues. I thank them for showing the blessedness, relief, and freedom that comes when everything is laid bare before Jesus Christ, as well as the peace, refreshing, and joy that follow when you let Him have His way. Thank you Joyce Meyer, Chip Ingram, and Focus on the Family. (This especially includes the time when Dr. James Dobson was part of the organization.)

PREFACE
My Story

DECEMBER 31, 2009—A night to remember and an evening of firsts. It was our church's first New Year's Eve service in our new building.

It was the first time our church's first praise-dance team performed.

It was the first time I praise-danced with a group.

It was the first time I executed a praise dance in front of people I knew well.

It was the first time I danced in front of members of the opposite sex.

It was the first time I felt remorsefully convicted about how I had treated my body.

It was the first time I realized that though I worshiped and praised God, I didn't worship and praise Him in the truest sense of the words.

It was the first time I experienced a rebuke from God that shook my core with such force that it brought me to my knees and unleashed a fountain of sorrow and instantaneous sobs of repentance.

Here is how it all went down.

I was dressed in my praise-dance outfit, prepared for our time to dance, when the choir performed one of my favorite songs, "Jesus Reigns" by Youthful Praise. This song makes me want to dance and leap with joy every time I hear it!

Already pumped and bursting with gratitude and excitement because of the many firsts that were happening—and because I was celebrating the end of another year—I felt joy that was off the charts! It was explosive! Praise burst forth from my body as if it came from a cannon, and the next thing I knew, I was dancing, twirling, and leaping all over the front of the church.

I danced so fiercely that my almost-two-hundred-pound body felt like only a hundred pounds! I felt as light-footed as a gazelle bounding along a mountainside, yet as robust as a newly formed tornado.

I liken the feeling I had to the way David must have felt when he danced out of his clothes after getting the ark back from Obed-Edom—except for one thing: I think David's stamina was greater than mine. He had traveled to Obed-Edom's house to get the ark, brought it back to his house, rejoiced the whole way back, sacrificed a bull and a calf, and after all of that he still had the energy to dance. His energy was still so strong that he danced right out of his clothes!

My energy, on the other hand, was short-lived. I hadn't done much of anything that whole day other than practice the dance a few times. Yet shortly after its release, my explosive praise fizzled out like a sparkler on the Fourth of July, quickly dwindling to an ember. Thank goodness I was near the altar. I was so worn out after my few minutes of unrestrained praise that I needed to lie on the altar—not to pray but to rest.

I lay on the altar, trying to catch my breath and stop that burning feeling that comes in your chest when you run fast and hard. As I gasped for air, not only could I not breathe, but my body felt like an anvil dropped from the sky. The gazelle was gone.

Oddly, I still wanted to dance. I still wanted to praise God. I still had an arsenal of praise expressions inside me that I hadn't unloaded. However, when I realized I was unable to continue praising God because of my exhaustion, I was left grief stricken and ashamed—ashamed that I had let my body, God's temple, get to this point.

I began weeping uncontrollably. For the first time I understood how I had defiled the temple of God—how giving in to my sinful desires had created a less-than-excellent place for my beloved Master to dwell. For that I felt deep remorse.

Over and over I begged God's forgiveness and apologized for all the selfish things I had done to the temple He had lent me. In that moment, I knew I would never behave the same way again. I realized the pain

I had inflicted upon my Father by how I had treated the gift He had given to me. This was the first time I felt a desire to change my sinful ways for His benefit and not my own.

In the midst of this, I heard His loving yet stern rebuke. I've since forgotten His exact words, but the gist was this: *You do not reflect me as best as you can.* Until that time, when people first saw me, I don't think they saw "good," "acceptable," or "pleasing." They saw my size and the fact that I was overweight.

His disappointment also conveyed, *When you talk about health and wellness, you ruin your own testimony.* This bruised my ego. As a health educator by occupation, and one who studies health and wellness for pleasure, how could I have the gall to talk about healthy habits and expect people to listen and change their behavior when I hadn't changed my own?

I was embarrassed, sorely grieved, and ashamed of how I represented myself and, more important, God. On the spot, I determined to change. I asked God to transform me.

Over the next several months, I studied Romans 12:1–2 and what it means to be transformed. This led to in-depth studies of these two verses. I desired, above all else, to offer my body to God as a sacrifice and for Him to be pleased with me.

Along the way, I journaled the things God showed and taught me. Four months later, God told me to put everything I had learned in a book and title it *Worship God! And Praise Away the Pounds!*

From December 31, 2009, until today, my life has definitely changed—in nature, function, and condition. Food no longer has the grip on me that it used to. I no longer dread moving this wonderful body God gave me. I no longer seek quick and easy fixes regarding my weight.

Now I seek God's way of doing things. Now I feel freer than I've ever felt in my life!

Don't get me wrong; this journey hasn't been, and still isn't, a piece of cake. It has been a constant battle—a battle between my flesh and my spirit. Many times a day I must choose between spiritual and fleshly, between life and death, between God's will and my own.

Sometimes I let my flesh get the upper hand, and when I do, I confess my sin, repent, and seek to discontinue doing that same thing again.

It's definitely a process. Thank God He is gracious, slow to anger, and plenteous in mercy. It is my utmost desire to be holy, acceptable, and pleasing to God by presenting my body to Him as a living sacrifice. It is my prayer that you may be transformed, delivered, and set free as I have been. May this book minister to you and assist you as you seek to *Worship God! And Praise Away the Pounds!*

INTRODUCTION
Choose

CHRISTIANS OFTEN FORGET we are "to be in the world, yet not of it." This said, we tend to function just as the world does. We approach situations and handle problems without consulting the Word of God, praying, or listening to the Holy Spirit. We do what comes naturally, behave according to tradition, or respond the way most everyone else does.

Everything we do, including the way we deal with weight and health issues, should lead us to God's ways rather than to the world's. Yet we follow mainstream diet plans, take diet pills, and buy in to weight-loss schemes. We forget the Word of God offers the answers to everything we could possibly face.

God's Word tells us how to live and what to do in *every* situation—even when it comes to our weight. When we go to God's Word, however, the priority should not be to get answers for things we want. As Christians, we should want to learn God's perspective and give Him what He wants.

Worship God! And Praise Away the Pounds! is a biblical approach to weight loss. It is not a typical diet book and isn't about how to lose weight per se. It is about how to follow God's leading and, in doing so, to make right choices, become healthier, and thus lose excess weight. It is a guide for how to achieve wellness in mind, body, and spirit.

Worship God! And Praise Away the Pounds! teaches you how to live a life that is pleasing to God, utilizing Romans 12:1–2 as its foundation: "I beseech you therefore, brethren, by the mercies of God, that you present your bodies a living sacrifice, holy, acceptable to God, which is your reasonable service. And do not be conformed to this world, but be transformed by the renewing of your mind, that you may prove what is that good and acceptable and perfect will of God."

In this book, these two verses are formed into seven strategies.

1. Present your body to God as a sacrifice.
2. Be devoted and consecrated to God.
3. Give God your reasonable service.
4. Don't conform to the world.
5. Be transformed.
6. Renew your mind.
7. Establish yourself as good, acceptable, and perfect.

These strategies point you to God's Word, teach you to live a life that pleases Him, free you from bondage, transform you, and establish you as "good, acceptable, and perfect."

So what do you want? Do you want to continue to try to figure things out on your own? Do you want to continue doing things the world's way (which only offers a temporary fix, at best)? Do you want to continue carrying excess weight? Do you want to keep your current habits and lifestyle? Do you want to continue living in bondage and straining to figure things out?

Or do you want the best solutions to your problems? Do you want to live a life surrendered to God? Do you want to live for His glory and not your own? Do you want to rid yourself of excess weight permanently? Do you want to surrender your will to God's and submit to His authority? Do you want the freedom and rest that come when you let God figure things out?

The choice is yours. If you choose God's way, the journey will not be easy, but it will be rewarding! You will experience freedom and peace like never before. Why? Because the great Jehovah (the great "I Am") will be guiding you, and He is everything you could ever need. As a matter of fact, two of His names are Jehovah Nissi ("Jehovah is my victory") and Jehovah Shalom ("the Lord is Peace").

Decide now. What do you want? Do you want to worship God and praise away the pounds? The way you live will signify your answer.

If you want to live God's way, continue reading!

Strategy One

PRESENT YOUR BODY TO GOD AS A SACRIFICE

Chapter 1

CHANGE

*H*OW TRULY SORRY I felt coming face-to-face with the reality that I had misrepresented God. Even worse, He was the one who broke the news to me. I knew I was overweight, obese by medical standards, but it didn't seem like a sin to be "fat." Though I didn't like my weight and wanted to be smaller, I didn't think it had any real bearing on my Christianity. As far as I was concerned, I was good: I loved God and loved people, I served Him, I studied His Word, and I desired to please Him. Even though I had many messed-up areas I constantly asked, even begged, God to change and heal, my heart toward Him was pure.

I didn't realize, however, the barrier my weight was to my Christian testimony. I couldn't see how my heavy appearance worked against what I told others about the freedom and deliverance that come from God. I'm sure they believed me, but I have no doubt my appearance left question marks somewhere in their hearts. This was especially true when I talked to people about health. I believe that as they listened, my words went through a filter of "Look at you; if you know so much, why are you so heavy?" At least this is what I thought when I heard health talks from people who were overweight.

When God spoke to me that New Year's Eve while I lay on the altar sobbing, after realizing how dissolute I'd been toward Him regarding my eating, I wanted to hide. I didn't want anyone to see me as I misrepresented God. But God, in His mercy and grace, didn't want me to hide but to stand firm in Him. He prompted me to begin studying Romans 12:1–2. These *verses held the keys to my breakthrough. To be free, I had to do something, give up something, and allow God to change my thinking about eating. I desperately wanted to end the madness involving my relationship with food.*

I beseech you therefore, brethren, by the mercies of God, that ye present your bodies a living sacrifice, holy, acceptable unto God, which is your reasonable service. And be not conformed to this world: but be ye transformed by the renewing of your mind, that ye may prove what is that good, and acceptable, and perfect, will of God.

—Romans 12:1–2 KJV

THE JOURNEY BEGINS

My journey to *Worship God! And Praise Away the Pounds!* began with Romans 12:1–2. I felt led to meditate on and study these verses before God even told me to write the book. These verses transformed me and changed me into someone pleasing to Him (even though I still have a long way to go). Since you've decided to worship God and praise away the pounds, Romans 12:1–2 is the place to start.

Jamieson, Fausset, and Brown's commentary states that Romans 12 is about the duties of the believer, with the first comprehensive duty described in verses 1–2.[1] Verse 1 is an appeal for believers (Christians) to *do* something—to give their bodies to God and live their lives a certain way. Believers are urged to do everything as if it were a sacrifice, something offered to God as an act of worship. I like the way *The Message* phrases it: "Take your everyday, ordinary life—your sleeping, eating, going-to-work, and walking around life—and place it before God as an offering." Simply put, our lives should be gifts—donations of worship—to God.

To help us better understand the meaning of worship, here are a few definitions.

- Reverence for a deity or sacred object; intense devotion to or esteem for a person or thing[2]
- Any action or attitude that expresses praise, love, and appreciation for God. Worship can be expressed through obedience.[3]
- To honor with extravagant love and *extreme submission*[4] (emphasis mine)

True worship toward God involves an intense devotion of attitude and action that expresses praise, love, appreciation, and most of all, obedience. If we truly worship God, we will honor Him with "extreme submission."

Submission to God involves the following actions:

- To surrender to the authority, discretion, or will of another[5]
- The act of yielding to power or authority; surrender of the person and power to the control or government of another[6]

When we submit to God, we surrender to His authority by allowing Him to make our decisions. Submitting isn't sharing leadership roles; it is resigning our power completely to God for Him to govern. If we add what we know about worship to the mix, we honor God by letting Him rule our lives with extreme submission—yielding to Him to the greatest possible degree. This means we will not exercise one iota of our power to rule our own lives.

I tried to visualize what extreme submission would look like. What came to mind was a picture of me in chains. This image, however, didn't fit the definition of submission because the chains represented holding me against my will. In this representation, instead of voluntarily surrendering my power, my power was involuntarily bound by the chains.

Then I saw it—an image of Jesus on the cross. Though He was nailed to the cross, His power wasn't bound. He could have annihilated His accusers, disintegrated the cross, and proved His omnipotence to the world, yet He didn't. He demonstrated extreme submission to the will of His Father and the saving power of the cross. All power existed within Him, yet He willingly surrendered to dying on the cross so we could be saved.

One last word must be understood for us to fully grasp our duty as believers, as well as how to be victorious over food and be found holy, acceptable, and pleasing to God: surrender.

To surrender is to give up oneself into the power of another; to yield; as the enemy, seeing no way of escape, surrendered at the first summons.[7] Although *surrender* means nearly the same as *submit*, there is one distinct difference. To submit involves willingly yielding our personal power to another because we *want* to. When we surrender, we yield because we *have* to, or because we see no other way out.

When we surrender, then, we are to give up our privileges to the power of another as if we have no way of escape. Looking a bit further into this definition, we can say that we, in our fleshly nature, are enemies with God and have no way of escaping death or the consequence of sin unless we surrender to Jesus Christ as our Lord and Savior.

Surrendering to God is what frees us from sin and death. If we give up our own desires and yield to His, we can be free from bondage to food and excess weight. When we surrender to God's will for our lives, not only will we be free, but we will be considered holy, acceptable, and pleasing because we are in His perfect will. We may not want to surrender our bodies to God. After all, we have the right to do what we please. As Christians, however, surrender is our spiritual act of worship, our reasonable service, our duty. For most of us, our personal rights and privileges regarding food and activity would look quite different if we were under God's command. Here are some examples from my own personal history of exercising rights and privileges that were not under God's command.

IRRATIONAL BEHAVIOR

At my worst, when I ate everything I wanted to eat and didn't consider God's will or that I had a duty to serve God with my body, I recall making insane choices regarding food. For instance, on a whim, my husband and I escaped to TJ Cinnamons to purchase sticky buns. Dementedly, I directed the server to scrape up all of the syrupy goo that was left from other buns and slap it in my container. I then proceeded to the free-toppings counter and slathered on as much cream cheese icing as would fit into my container. It tasted good going down, but afterward I felt sick and shaky from the sugar overload. Still, I foolishly repeated this act again and again.

On another occasion I went to a favorite pizza place and ordered two medium pizzas with everything plus extra cheese. My husband and I ate all of it, and I ate just as much as he did. Other times I bought a pound of fudge, got another pound free, and ate most of it by myself.

Once my husband and I went to a famous seafood and steak house with an all-you-can-eat buffet. I madly scarfed down three or four plates of food. I ate more than my stomach could hold; food had accumulated to the top of my esophagus. I had little room in my lungs and diaphragm because my stomach was so distended, which made it extremely difficult to breathe. Every time I moved, I felt as if I would vomit. The short walk to the restroom took an extended amount of time since I needed to move slowly to prevent throwing up in the restaurant. As soon as I got to the toilet, food gushed out of my mouth like a spewing hydrant.

CONVICTION

As embarrassing as it is to admit this repulsive behavior, I'm mortified to say that these were some of the ways I "joyfully" yet secretly behaved until God began to convict me. The conviction caused gradual shifts in my behavior. I went from being a food maniac to a person with an almost complete lack of self-control before I understood the wantonness of my actions.

Worse, I was a Christian engaging in this type of rash behavior. As a matter of fact, I thought it was fun to go places and eat like a pig until my heart was "content" and my stomach engorged. I didn't think about the internal damage I could have done by eating so much food. I didn't even think about what was happening to my health and my weight. Foolishly, all I thought about was what I wanted to eat next and how good it would taste.

Though I didn't realize it then, I know now I was killing myself. By exercising my rights and privileges to eat whatever I wanted, I was leading myself to an early grave. God waited all the while in the background for me to surrender my will to His so He could show me a better way—the way to life and health.

God's ways are not our ways, and His thoughts are not our thoughts. Only He knows everything. Then why do we foolishly ignore Him? We act as if we know everything simply because we have a personal will, but following our own will gets us into trouble every time. How can we *not* get into trouble surrendering to our own will, then, when our very nature is sinful? Since this is the case, it stands to reason that acting on what we will, will cause us to sin. God, on the other hand, has a sinless nature. When we surrender to His will, we will be led down the path of righteousness and sinlessness.

What about you? What are your desires? What has your will led you to do? Has it led you to life or death? In our flesh, we head straight toward the path of destruction. When we follow the voice of the Holy Spirit, we are on the path to life—a life that is healthy and good.

SURRENDER

Let's let the Holy Spirit rule and guide us in our decisions. He wants to lead us on the right path. We need to ask God what to do about everything—nothing is too small or too silly to take to Him.

After realizing my need to seek the Holy Spirit for His guidance, I stopped following diet plans and the things I had learned in my many health classes. I began asking God how to eat. I started opening my refrigerator and saying, "God, show me what to eat." Whatever I felt I heard Him say was what I ate. I didn't measure amounts or analyze whether I needed more or less of one kind of food or another. I just ate what I felt the Lord told me.

Sometimes as I pulled things out of my refrigerator, I heard a small voice say, "Not that" or "Put that away." Other times the same voice told me to get the very food that previously I was told to not eat. There seemed to be no set pattern for what I could or couldn't eat. Some days I could have a dessert or something sweet, other days I couldn't. Some days I could eat fruit, other days I felt led not to. The Holy Spirit taught me to surrender my will and submit to His authority. He taught me how to listen to the voice of God and to check with my body to see how it felt after I'd eaten.

It had never occurred to me to check with my body to see how it responded to what I ate. I ate whatever my mind dictated, and my body's response was of no concern. God taught me to connect my eating to my senses. He taught me to think about what I was eating and to notice the pleasure or pain connected to it. I began to enjoy flavors I hadn't enjoyed before and find pleasure in textures I had previously ignored. I began to realize that some foods made me feel jittery, but others gave me energy. Some foods digested easily, but others caused gas, bloating, and constipation.

God, in His infinite wisdom, opened up a whole new world to me regarding food. He helped me to see what brought fulfillment and life, as well as pain and death. When we listen and yield to the wisdom of God, we learn many wonderful things.

In summary, it is our Christian duty to live lives of worship to God. We do this by surrendering our will and submitting to His authority so we can be found holy, pleasing, and acceptable to Him, which is our reasonable service.

Call to Action

1. How can you improve your worship to God (see definitions of worship, submission, and surrender in the chapter)?
2. What do you need to surrender to God?
3. What will your life look like if you submit to God's authority?
4. Now that you've reflected on these questions, what is one action God is prompting you to take?

Father, please forgive me for doing whatever I want rather than what pleases You. Forgive me for making choices with the precious body You've given me that lead me to death and cause me to be irreverent toward You. Help me to love You more than I love the things that please me. In Jesus' name I pray. Amen.

Chapter 2

PUT GOD FIRST

*F*OR MORE THAN *ten years, I have made it a point to connect with God before I get out of bed—except when I really have to use the restroom first! Before my feet even hit the floor, I pull out my Bible (sometimes more than one), Scripture cards, notebooks, journals, devotionals, and whatever else I've been reading or studying. I keep everything beside my bed so I don't have to get up.*

I don't know how or when I began this habit (I'm sure it had something to do with being desperate to change), but I must connect with God before I do anything else. My connection with Him is what stabilizes me, grounds me, and prevents me from reverting to my natural, messed-up tendencies.

> "But seek first his kingdom and his righteousness, and all these things will be given to you as well."
>
> —Matthew 6:33 NIV

FIRST THINGS FIRST

God tells us in His Word to seek Him *first*. How much plainer can things get? First means *first*. Before all else. Above all. Foremost. The beginning. Number one. God should be first, our priority—not family, spouse, friends, work, or even ourselves.

We tend to forget this truth and fall into the natural rhythm of life, letting the urgency of unplanned events and emergencies dictate our priorities and focus. We react to whatever comes rather than act intentionally to order our lives and attend to what is truly important and cannot wait.

Many activities we consider to be important can wait. For example, going to the gym to work out may be important, but it can wait. Getting a morning dose of caffeine to wake you up may be important, but it too can wait.

On the other hand, some important things cannot wait—taking a hurt child to the emergency room, for example, or paying your electric bill before your electricity gets shut off. Putting off a medical emergency or financial obligation may bring dangerous consequences. Likewise, we experience consequences if we wait to connect with God until we've done everything else. By the end of the day, we will have already faced (and likely) failed temptations to lose our tempers, gossip, or do other things we will regret. To avoid those consequences, we must connect with God—joining our minds, hearts, and spirits to Him—before we begin the tasks of our day.

MAKE THE CONNECTION

Here are several tried-and-tested ways to connect with God each day.

Pray. To pray means to communicate with God by giving thanks to Him, expressing adoration of Him, or making requests known to Him. We can pray the Lord's Prayer, pray passages straight from the Bible, or even pray in our own words. Of course, communication involves two-way interaction, so we must take time to listen to God as well.

Meditate. To meditate means to ponder, to reflect, or to focus our thoughts. The purpose of meditation is to worship God or to receive instruction, motivation, encouragement, or transformation.[1] We can reflect on one or more words (*hope, mercy,* or *faith,* for example) or verses from the Bible, ponder the attributes of God, focus on His words of encouragement or instruction, or contemplate how we want our lives to look in the future.

Read. To read means to gain an understanding of printed information. Read Scripture or other materials like devotionals or Christian literature to learn more about God, His Word, and His will for your life.

10

Study. To study means to examine closely, scrutinize, analyze, or give careful consideration to information. Study Scripture by using a Bible, a concordance, an English or Bible dictionary, or other resources. The goal is to fully understand what we read, discover deeper meaning, and apply what we read to our lives. Doing so will make us stronger Christians who are able to discern and understand truth.

Memorize. To memorize means to commit something to memory, to learn something so we can repeat it verbatim. Memorizing Scripture can help us when we face times of trouble, danger, or fear. Being able to recall Scripture can reestablish us when unexpected circumstances knock us off our feet, ground us when we feel unsure of how to proceed, and give us courage in the face of adversity.

Wait. To wait means to be still, to remain inactive, or to stay where we are until we receive the go-ahead to move. Waiting is a difficult yet necessary task for believers in Christ. When we wait on God to direct us, rather than following our own path, we receive God's very best.

When we're faced with a tough decision, we should wait until we receive clear direction from God—through reading His Word, by confirmation from a man or woman of God, or through biblical literature. Sometimes we hear God telling us yes or no, but we ignore Him because His answer doesn't align with what we want. Other times we truly don't know what to do. For example, we may wonder about taking a job that pays better than our current job but would move us away from family and friends. Do we take the job, knowing it would help us economically? Or do we pass up the opportunity to keep our children near the people who know and love them? Both choices have pros and cons, and both require us to wait on God to hear what He wants us to do.

When we've asked God for guidance but we don't receive a clear answer, He could be saying no, He could be saying to do nothing yet, or He may be telling us to do whatever we choose as long as we don't violate the principles in His Word.

CHOOSE THE LEVEL OF CONNECTION

We have many ways of connecting with God and also many levels of connecting with Him. Perhaps we touch base with Him for a few brief minutes, deeply connect by spending hours with Him, or something in between. Regardless of the way or the level, Scripture says to seek Him first, prior to everything else.

As I mentioned, I need to connect with God at a deep level first thing in the morning, before my mind becomes cluttered with daily demands, mental to-do lists, decision making, inappropriate thoughts, traffic, insecurity issues, and so forth. I need to meet with my heavenly Father while my mind is fresh and alert.

For you, however, morning may not be your best time to learn well or absorb large amounts of content. Even so, you still need to connect with God in some way at the start of your day. Spend a few minutes praying, reading, or meditating on a verse or two of Scripture. Then when your brain is alert and keen, perhaps at your lunch break or bedtime, connect with Him on a deeper level.

WHY PUT GOD FIRST?

God asks us to put Him first for two main reasons: (1) so we can obey His commands, and (2) so He can bless us.

Let's look at Matthew 6:33 in a few different translations and versions of the Bible.

- The King James Version says God wants to "add" to us.
- *The Message* says He wants to meet our "everyday human concerns."
- The Amplified Bible says He wants to give "all these things taken together."
- The New Living Translation says He will give us "everything [we] need."
- The New American Standard Bible says "all these things will be added" to us.

The wording changes a bit from version to version, but Matthew 6:33 boils down to the fact that God wants to bless us when we put Him first.

Put God first and make time for Him. If you do, you will be living in blessed obedience to His Word.

Call to Action

1. Based on your actions, what are your priorities?
2. What changes do you need to make so connecting with God becomes a higher priority?
3. What changes are you willing to make? When will you make them?
4. How do you see your life improving as a result of these changes?
5. What action is God prompting you to take?

Lord, please help me to put You first, before everything else. Please help me not to get so caught up in busyness that I forget to seek You. Remind me that You have the answers to everything that concerns me and that if I connect with You, You will help me and direct me, and all will be well. In Jesus' name. Amen.

STEPS TO STAY ON TRACK

I'D BEEN ON a good roll, completing daily logs of my eating, activity, and sleeping. I had even started setting daily goals and then evaluating my success every evening. This gave me something to aim at and kept me consciously and subconsciously on track. Then one weekend, I opted not to fill out my logs, because the past few weekends I hadn't kept up with everything and most of my logs were incomplete.

I thought I was doing myself a favor by not wasting paper. (At least that's what I told myself.) Instead of staying on the right track and holding myself accountable by completing my logs, I reverted back to some old patterns. I ate more of the foods I normally wouldn't eat and less of those I normally ate. My fleshly nature rose up and took advantage of the situation. It pushed past its normal limits and restraints and sought to have more. This started on a Friday night with a few Twizzlers and M&Ms. Things escalated to two pieces of cake on Saturday and three cookies on Sunday!

> Leave no [such] room or foothold for the devil [give no opportunity to him].
>
> —Ephesians 4:27 AMP

NEVER TRUST YOUR SINFUL NATURE

What was my problem that weekend? I took away my accountability, which opened the door for my fleshly nature to do what it naturally does: rise against the Spirit. If only I hadn't assumed my fleshly self was under control and that it no longer went against its self-serving nature! My wrong assumption led to unleashing an animal that is hard to tame and seeks to wound with deadly poison. Remaining in the Spirit would have reminded me not to give a foothold—not even a toehold—of opportunity to the devil.

Ephesians 4:27 reminds me of a story I heard about a snake that asked to be carried up a mountain and promised not to bite its escort. The trusting person believed the snake had changed its nature, since the snake had *promised* it wouldn't bite him. The man struggled up the mountain carrying the deceitful serpent on his back. Once he reached the summit, the snake bit him! The gullible man asked why, and the viper replied, "Never trust a snake!"

We can never trust our flesh. It does what comes naturally—it strives against the Spirit. However, if we don't give room for our flesh to flourish, it cannot gain strength. We must keep the door closed to our flesh so our labor in the Spirit is not wasted.

BE ACCOUNTABLE

The good news is we can avoid being "bitten." We can set up barriers against our flesh by establishing systems of accountability to help us take responsibility for ourselves and our actions.

"Accountability is a concept in ethics and governance with several meanings. It is often used synonymously with such concepts as responsibility, answerability, blameworthiness, liability, and other terms associated with the expectation of account giving."[1] I like this definition because it relates to ethics (conduct and values) and governance (management and rule). Both play major roles in our Christian walk. We should be under the governance of the Holy Spirit, who guides us toward proper conduct and godly values.

Governance is also defined as "the art of conceptually identifying probable causes of failures in the system and ensuring preventive action to avoid damage."[2] This definition sums up why we need systems of accountability, as well as how to set them up.

Why do we need accountability? We need it so we do not fail in our efforts to present our bodies to God as sacrifices that are holy and acceptable. We also need it to help avoid the damage that is sure to ensue when our flesh rules.

If our ultimate goal is to be found as holy, acceptable, and pleasing to God, then we will do everything we can to ensure it happens. How can we do this? By identifying probable events that may cause us to fail and then setting up preventive measures that will help us avoid the damage.

MANAGE YOUR BEHAVIOR

Let's take a closer look at what we mean by accountability and governance. For example, if I want to make good food choices, my first step is to identify probable events (foods) that may cause me to fall. Since certain junk foods are weaknesses for me, I need to clearly identify what they are: fresh-baked gourmet cakes, cookies, and brownies; Sheridan's frozen custard and Paciugo gelato (Italian ice cream); fresh-baked bread and *real* butter. (Ignorance of your weaknesses sets you up for failure. If you don't know your weaknesses, you will neglect to position yourself to avoid them.)

After identifying the probable events that could cause me to fall, I need to set up preventive measures. I do this by being keenly aware of the danger zones. This means I first need to stay away from Whole Foods, Panera, and St. Louis Bread Company's bakery section. When I'm out, I need to forego driving by Sheridan's, Paciugo, and sweets shops. When I avoid these places, I'm stronger, and it is easier to resist temptation.

Other preventive measures for me include carrying limited cash so I don't have the money to buy desserts, making a list before going grocery shopping and sticking to the list, and asking my husband and baker friends not to show their love by bringing me enticing sweets. When I'm at a function where there are lots of desserts, instead of going through the dessert line myself, I have my husband pick out something for me, or I ask him to tell me the choices and have him get one thing I want. Looking at everything could mean losing self-control!

When I'm at a buffet, I scan the desserts and put tiny amounts of everything I want on a small plate (or on a small portion of a regular plate if dessert plates are not available). I do not get a plateful, but rather the equivalent of one serving. Occasionally, I allow myself two servings. Usually when I do, I leave some on my plate.

Another way I make success more likely is to keep a daily log of the foods I eat. Doing so keeps me aware of the amounts of beneficial and nonbeneficial foods I am eating. I set a goal of eating at least a combination of five fruits and vegetables each day. I limit grain products because they make my blood-sugar levels unstable, and I don't feel well when I eat too many. My permitted allotment of sweets depends on what the Holy Spirit tells me is OK. Sometimes I can have one (rarely two or more because it can send me into a dessert frenzy), and other times I'm directed to have none, when my body has begun to react negatively to excess sugar consumption.

As you can see, a variety of measures helps me to manage my behavior and practice godly conduct so I don't undo the painful toil it took to lose the weight I've lost so far.

Most of the accountability measures I have in place are self-directed. Since I am a fairly disciplined person, self-accountability works for me—although not totally. I need to be loosely accountable to others too.

GET HELP FROM OTHERS

Because I have a strong tendency to be a people pleaser, too much other-accountability drives me to strive to please them rather than God. But certain people do know I am working to please God and to present my body as a living sacrifice that is holy and acceptable to Him. Just knowing that people know, and are watching me, helps me to stay in line.

You, however, may have a different personality, one in which self-accountability is challenging. You may need someone, or someones, to keep a fire under you to help you govern yourself responsibly. If this is what you need, don't be embarrassed. The more honest you are about who you are and what you need (or don't need), the more successful you will be in your endeavors.

If you need others to hold you accountable, you can do this by

- reporting to them daily, weekly, or biweekly (for example, Mondays and Wednesdays);
- being open and honest with them and allowing them the same freedom with you;

- giving them permission to randomly call you and ask how you are doing;
- giving them permission to ask you pointed questions;
- writing down your behavior and asking them to comment on it;
- spending regular time with them so they can witness your behavior in various contexts;
- asking them to pray for you.

Be sure to select mature believers who are knowledgeable in the Word, disciplined, and not afraid to hold you accountable.

ACCOUNTABILITY IN SCRIPTURE

Accountability is a scriptural principle, illustrated in Galatians 6:1–5: "Brethren, if a man is overtaken in any trespass, you who are spiritual restore such a one in a spirit of gentleness, considering yourself lest you also be tempted. Bear one another's burdens, and so fulfill the law of Christ. For if anyone thinks himself to be something, when he is nothing, he deceives himself. But let each one examine his own work, and then he will have rejoicing in himself alone, and not in another. For each one shall bear his own load."

Verse 1 makes me think of accountability in the form of ethics and governance we discussed earlier in the chapter. We Christians are instructed to submit ourselves to others' authority as well as to be the authority to others who submit to our rule (governance). In both cases, we are to maintain godly values (ethics).

Verse 2 sums up the second part of the definition of accountability, "It is often used synonymously with such concepts as responsibility, answerability, blameworthiness, liability, and other terms associated with the expectation of account giving." We are to help bear one another's burdens.

Verse 3 simply means that we are foolish to think we can be successful alone on this Christian journey. We deceive ourselves if we think we don't need others to help us. God created us to be in relationship.

Verses 4–5 relate to governance, "the art of conceptually identifying probable causes of failures in the system and ensuring preventive action to avoid damage." We are to pay careful attention to what we do because we are responsible for our conduct, and we'll eventually have to give an account to God.

In summary, we need to identify probable events that can cause us to fail, and then set up preventive measures that will help us avoid the damage. We do this by setting up systems of self- and other-accountability. We need accountability to keep our fleshly nature in check so we can stay on the path of holiness. Accountability keeps us from falling and from being deceived.

Call to Action

1. In what areas do you need accountability?
2. What are some preventive actions you need to take?
3. List some potential accountability partners.
4. How soon are you willing to start? (What would God say about your start date?)
5. What action is God prompting you to take?

God, please give me the courage and desire to overtake my flesh. Help me be willing to do whatever it takes to get my flesh under submission to the Spirit. Send people my way to whom I can be accountable, and bless me to live a holy life so others will want to be accountable to me. In Jesus' name. Amen.

Chapter 4

THE IMPORTANCE OF WATER

I DRINK A lot of water—probably more than the average person. For example, last summer my husband and I, along with some friends, went to an outdoor concert. Within the five hours or so we were there, I sucked down seventy-six ounces of water—and wanted more! My husband took only a few swigs of one of my bottles and was fine. Others around me held on to one bottle of water (or soda) the entire time. Why the differences?

I drink water throughout the day—no sodas, juices, or other beverages. When I know I'll be out for a while, I take extra water with me. When I don't drink enough, I feel weak and nauseated, I get a headache, and my shoulder muscles feel achy and "dried out." Water plays an important part in nourishing my body and keeping me feeling healthy.

> Joyfully you'll pull up buckets of water from the wells of salvation.
> —Isaiah 12:3 MSG

WATER'S BENEFITS

Needing lots of water isn't a bad thing. It may be an inconvenience, but it's an important part of life—physically and spiritually. Let's take a closer look.

We know all living things require water to live and thrive. Our bodies consist of sixty to seventy percent water. A person can live only three to ten days without water. Without enough water, waste and toxins begin to build up in your body. Water helps regulate body temperature, keeps our bodies cool through perspiration, acts as a lubricant to our joints, cushions our organs, and helps remove waste. No one would disagree that water is essential for our physical health and well-being. Now let's look at water's spiritual connections.

WATER'S SPIRITUAL CONNECTION

In Genesis 1, the Spirit of God hovered over the waters, God separated the waters of the heavens from the waters of the earth, and He gathered all of the water on the earth into one place. God told the waters on the earth to teem with all kinds of living creatures, and then He told these creatures to reproduce and fill the waters. Here we see water's connection to life's development.

In Genesis 7, God used water in the form of a flood to destroy the earth, after He saw how corrupt it had become. He destroyed everything except for the people and animals aboard Noah's ark. In Genesis 9, God established a covenant with Noah and all living creatures that He would never again destroy the earth by floodwater. Here we have water's connection to mass destruction.

In Exodus, God performed a number of miraculous acts using water. In chapter 7, because Pharaoh wouldn't let the Israelites go, God caused the water of the Nile River to turn to blood. In chapter 14, God parted the Red Sea so the Israelites could walk through on dry ground. He closed it again so the Egyptians were swept into the sea. In chapter 15, God instructed Moses to throw a stick into some bitter water to make it sweet so the thirsty Israelites could drink it. In chapter 17, when there was no water for the people to drink, God instructed Moses to strike a rock with his staff—and out came water. Here we observe water's connection to human deliverance.

In Matthew 3, Jesus was baptized in water. Though He needed no repentance or cleansing from sin, He was baptized to show He completely identified himself with our sin. Baptism signifies spiritual cleansing and rebirth. Here we see water as a divine detergent.

In Matthew 14, Jesus walked on water, revealing His transcendent power over nature. He then invited Peter to walk on water with Him. Here we see water being used in a miraculous demonstration. Jesus also used water to perform His very first miracle. In John 2, Jesus told servants to fill some jars with water. They obeyed. Then He told them to draw some out and take it to the master of the banquet. Again, they followed His instructions, and instead of water the master of the banquet sampled wine. Through this miracle, Jesus revealed His glory. Here we see water's connection to a supernatural display of God's glory.

Jesus referred to himself as living water in John 4 and 7. By this, He was referring to himself as the one who gives eternal life. Here we see Jesus' connection to water as the life-giving drink.

In John 13, Jesus demonstrated an act of servitude when He took a basin of water and washed His disciples' feet, a servant's job. Here we see water being used to serve humankind.

In John 19, during Jesus' crucifixion, a soldier pierced Jesus' side, and out poured blood and water. First John 5:6–8 (NLT) also talks about blood and water: "And Jesus Christ was revealed as God's Son by his baptism in water and by shedding his blood on the cross—not by water only, but by water and blood. And the Spirit, who is truth, confirms it with his testimony. So we have these three witnesses—the Spirit, the water, and the blood—and all three agree."

Jesus' ministry began with His water baptism and ended with His bloody crucifixion. During His ministry, He embodied the Spirit as the Son of God in human form. The Spirit, blood, and water all play an important role in our salvation.

From the above scenarios, we see the following truths:

- Water aids in life's development.
- Water can play a part in mass destruction.
- Water served as part of people's deliverance.
- Water acts as a divine detergent.
- Water can be the agent for miraculous demonstrations.
- Water revealed Jesus' glory.
- Water is a life-giving drink.
- Water faithfully serves humankind.
- Water plays an important role in our salvation.

Water is essential if we want to live an acceptable life that is pleasing to God.

DRINK WATER

If our ultimate goal is to please God and to do His will, then we will drink plenty of water. We will drink it for physiological reasons such as to flush out toxins, keep us hydrated, and keep our bodies cool and our joints lubricated. We will also "drink" plenty of water for spiritual reasons. Drinking in the water of the Word (Eph. 5:26) provides us with spiritual knowledge, refreshment, salvation, restoration, and transformation.

Do not neglect drinking water. Even if you don't like it, your body needs it. Our natural self would probably prefer something more tasty and sweet, like soda or juice, yet too much of these are not good for us. Even when our spiritual selves prefer to have what *we* want and do things *our own* way rather than God's, some things may be permissible for us but not beneficial (1 Cor. 6:12).

Individuals require different amounts of water. As I shared in the beginning of the chapter, I need more water than most people I know. This is true for me both physically and spiritually. If I want my body to feel well, I must drink lots of water. If I want my spirit to be strong and able to withstand the trials of the day, I need heavy doses of the water of the Word.

Drink more water. Saturate yourself with its physical and spiritual benefits. Don't allow yourself to miss out on the good things it has to offer. Water saves! If we truly recognize its marvelous life-giving benefits, we will: "joyfully ... pull up buckets of water from the wells of salvation" (Isa. 12:3 MSG).

Call to Action

1. Are you taking in beneficial amounts of water, physically *and* spiritually?
2. What are some things you need to change regarding your physical and spiritual water intake? (Spiritual examples: Have you been baptized? Do you serve others in a way that is comparable to washing their feet?)
3. What do you crave more than physical and/or spiritual water?

4. Name two things you can do to increase your physical and spiritual water intake.

5. What action is God prompting you to take?

Lord, please help me to understand the importance of water for my spiritual and physical body. Help me not to ignore the importance of it, but to have the desire to do what I can to drink water in a way that pleases You. In Jesus' name. Amen.

Chapter 5

GET MOVING

*S*EVERAL YEARS AGO, *while taking one of many classes on how to improve my health, I was asked my top three reasons for not exercising. Without hesitation, I said, "I don't have time, I'm usually too tired, and I don't like to."*

In this class, my excuses didn't fly. I was asked to find specific ways to get around these barriers. To fit exercise into my busy schedule, I said I could get up ten minutes earlier, exercise while sitting or watching TV, and exercise before getting into bed. To get around being too tired, I said I would exercise regardless of how I felt, which more than likely would energize me. To combat not liking to exercise, I said I would change my attitude or find an exercise I like to do. Of course, these things were much easier said than done.

My solutions offered a temporary—very temporary—fix. After only a couple of weeks, I was back to my old habits. I was unable to sustain the changes because I wasn't truly motivated to change. What I really wanted was to lose weight while continuing to eat and do as I pleased. Since I didn't take seriously the benefits of exercise to my physical and spiritual health, I ended up heavier and experienced a number of avoidable health problems.

Do you not know that your bodies are temples of the Holy Spirit, who is in you, whom you have received from God? You are not your own; you were bought at a price. Therefore honor God with your bodies.
—1 Corinthians 6:19–20 NIV

A SPIRITUAL CHANGE

It took me years to thoroughly grasp the importance of exercise. I took numerous classes on how to improve my health, as well as classes on how to teach others how to improve theirs. I received numerous trainings and certifications on the subject. I read books and articles and even worked in the field of health. I also read books about what the Bible has to say on the subject, yet I made no drastic improvements regarding exercise.

Thank God, a conversion took place! I don't know exactly what brought about the change, but I know it occurred during the time I began to desire to live in a way that was acceptable and pleasing to my Lord. I believe it was the conviction of the Holy Spirit, because something inside me clicked and helped me see errors in my ways, causing me to actually desire exercise.

The Holy Spirit did a work in me that caused me to discern truths I had read and superficially understood but hadn't fully grasped. As in the scripture stated above, I came to realize my body is a holy temple that belongs to God.

A temple is a place where God resides, and I was not taking care of God's dwelling place. Instead, I was destroying it, while still expecting a holy and righteous God to live in a place that was overfed a steady diet of unhealthy foods and received little to no exercise. This made His temple, my body, a place that couldn't wholly worship, because it was overweight, sluggish, and too improperly nourished for optimal reverence.

Would a holy and righteous God want to dwell in a place filled with clutter, greed, and a lack of self-restraint, a temple in which His host could barely breathe, move, or perform His will? Regrettably, I permitted my loving Savior to dwell in such an unclean place. Things had to change.

BENEFITS OF EXERCISE

God helped me realize the health benefits of physical activity. Exercise reduces stress by releasing feel-good hormones, counters anxiety and depression, decreases tension, and helps elevate our mood. Ironically, regular exercise reduces the pain of arthritis and fibromyalgia, as well as improves the negative impact of chronic diseases such as diabetes and heart disease.

Jordan and Nicki Rubin write that exercise increases the body's natural virus-killing cells and contributes to improved mental health.[1] According to the American Association of Christian Counselors' Health and Wellness Coaching training program, thirty minutes of daily exercise burns calories, improves circulation, stimulates cholesterol metabolism, helps drain the lymphatic system, raises HDL (good cholesterol), burns stress chemicals, increases endorphins (the feel-good hormones), improves energy levels, and strengthens and tones muscles. Jane L. Murray, MD, lectured that along with everything just listed, daily movement regulates appetite, improves lipid profiles, decreases blood pressure, improves blood-sugar control, helps with relaxation, and improves sleep. Scott Conard, MD, sums it up best: "Exercise is the best medicine for the body."[2]

OBSTACLES TO EXERCISE

I used to think of exercise as work. The word itself made me think of a dreaded chore. Dr. Conard suggests thinking of exercise as play. This is a more fun way to look at it. Personally, I'm more motivated to have fun than do work. Hence, I now think of exercise as doing something fun that makes me feel good. Burning fat and calories while taking a walk to enjoy nature, connecting with my family while playing outdoor games, or doing Zumba (a mix of Latin, Brazilian, and African dance aerobics that's like a dance party) are some forms of play for me.

Before I began regularly moving my body, I liked sitting around and not getting much exercise. I'd *think* about going outside and enjoying nature, playing with my family, dancing, or being more active, but I couldn't seem to motivate myself to do it. Dr. Conard says the less we move, the less we want to move and the less we are able to move. I found this to be absolutely true! When I wasn't active, I didn't want to be more active. Now that I'm more active, I want to move, and I don't feel as well when I'm less active.

EXERCISING IS EASY

I looked up synonyms for *exercise*, and this is what I found: *stretch, bend, pull, tug, hike, work, muscle tone, labor, strain, loosen up, drill, execute, perform exercises, practice, take a walk, work out, warm up, train, move the body.*[3]

As you look at this list, even if you consider yourself a nonmover, you can see that you already get daily exercise. The natural stretching we do before we get out of bed, walking to the restroom, showering, dressing, and preparing meals all involve exercise! Most of us simply need to add another minute (or more) of movement to some of the things we already do. Then, if we add a few minutes of something fun, we'll be on our way to getting enough activity that will benefit our health. Doesn't this make exercising sound more doable?

Look again at the synonyms for exercise. Now think about the different kinds of activities you've heard or read about in the Bible. There was working, fighting, dancing, playing musical instruments, building, partying, shepherding, plowing, planting, harvesting, gleaning, cooking, rowing boats, fishing, hiking, and lots and lots of walking. *All* of these activities are considered exercise.

God designed us to move. Why else would He have formed us with muscles, joints, and bones? Why else would He have given us strength, flexibility, and ability? Why else would He have wired our bodies so exercise has such an influence on our health? He created our bodies to be self-sufficient, with God-given capabilities to handle various levels and types of physical activity.

BIBLICAL TRUTHS ABOUT OUR BODIES

So far, we've looked at a number of physiological reasons why it is important to move our bodies. Let's look at some things the Bible has to say. "So here's what I want you to do, God helping you: Take your everyday, ordinary life—your sleeping, eating, going-to-work, and walking-around life—and place it before God as an offering. Embracing what God does for you is the best thing you can do for him" (Rom. 12:1 MSG).

Everything we do should be presented to God as an offering or act of worship. Whatever we do with our bodies should glorify Him. "Therefore I always exercise and discipline myself [mortifying my body, deadening my carnal affections, bodily appetites, and worldly desires, endeavoring in all respects] to have a clear (unshaken, blameless) conscience, void of offense toward God and toward men" (Acts 24:16 AMP).

Since God has given us authority over our flesh, we have the power and ability within us to resist our appetite and the desire for inactivity. "God-loyal people don't stay down long; Soon they're up on their feet, while the wicked end up flat on their faces" (Prov. 24:16 MSG).

If we are truly trying to please God, we will not easily give up when we fall into temptation and into our old habits of laziness. Instead, we will repeatedly try again. "But He gives us more and more grace (power of the Holy Spirit, to meet this evil tendency and all others fully)" (James 4:6 AMP).

As we surrender our bodies to God, He'll give us more and more grace to resist laziness. "And we, who with unveiled faces reflect the Lord's glory, are being transformed into his likeness with ever-increasing glory, which comes from the Lord, who is the Spirit" (2 Cor. 3:18 NIV).

The more we seek and obey His will, the more we will be changed into His likeness—we will radiate His glory! "If you don't know what you're doing, pray to the Father. He loves to help. You'll get his help, and won't be condescended to when you ask for it" (James 1:5 MSG).

If we don't know what exercises are best for us, we can ask God. He'll show us what to do! "Whether you turn to the right or to the left, your ears will hear a voice behind you, saying, 'This is the way; walk in it'" (Isa. 30:21 NIV).

Whatever exercise we do, God will tell us whether it is good for us or not. The Holy Spirit will speak to our spirit, and we will know deep down whether we should continue. "For those who are according to the flesh and are controlled by its unholy desires set their minds on and pursue those things which gratify the flesh, but those who are according to the Spirit and are controlled by the desires of the Spirit set their minds on and seek those things which gratify the [Holy] Spirit" (Rom. 8:5 AMP).

When we cater to our own will and desires, we will never please God. "So then those who are living the life of the flesh [catering to the appetites and impulses of their carnal nature] cannot please or satisfy God, or be acceptable to Him" (Rom. 8:8 AMP). But when we are seeking God and His ways through reading and studying His Word and through the hearing and teaching of it, we will begin to desire to do things that please Him. "Now all glory to God, who is able, through his mighty power at work within us, to accomplish infinitely more than we might ask or think" (Eph. 3:20 NLT). God helps us behave in a way that pleases Him through His power, the Holy Spirit who works in us. "But thanks be to God, Who gives us the victory [making us conquerors] through our Lord Jesus Christ" (1 Cor. 15:57 AMP).

God has already given us the victory over everything that tries to defeat us. We can overcome inactivity and laziness if we choose to. "And I am convinced and sure of this very thing, that He Who began a good work in you will continue until the day of Jesus Christ [right up to the time of His return], developing [that good work] and perfecting and bringing it to full completion in you" (Phil. 1:6 AMP). We can have confidence, knowing that if the Holy Spirit sparks a desire in us to increase our daily exercise, He will continue to develop us in this area until we accomplish His will. "Brothers, I do not consider myself yet to have taken hold of it. But one thing I do: Forgetting what is behind and straining toward what is ahead, I press on toward the goal to win the prize for which God has called me heavenward in Christ Jesus" (Phil. 3:13–14 NIV).

Dear brother or sister, press, strain, and endeavor to do the things God has called you to do—one of which is to exercise your body. Use the talents and abilities He's given you, rather than letting them go to waste and burying them. If you use the abilities He's given you, He'll give you more. In the end, you'll be able to hear, "Well done, good and faithful servant!" (see Matt. 25:14–30.)

SIMPLE WAYS TO BE ACTIVE

Here are some practical ways to be more active.

- Stretch your entire body upon arising.
- Do one to two minutes of arm circles, toe touches, and/or leg lifts before showering and again after getting dressed.

- Do leg lifts, arm reaches, or other activity while sitting.
- Sit on a balance ball while watching TV (it strengthens your core muscles).
- Jump rope, march, or walk in place while watching TV.
- During commercials, do sit-ups or wall push-ups.
- Park farther away.
- Walk the long way from one place to another.
- Make individual trips, rather than consolidating trips, in your home.
- If you have stairs, make extra trips up and down.
- Rather than standing or sitting, walk or march in place.
- Purchase a fun ten-minute workout video.
- Take a dance class.
- Learn one of the martial arts.
- Dance while listening to the radio.
- Join your local gym.
- Be active with your friends.
- Walk during your breaks or as part of your lunch break.
- Walk around your neighborhood.
- Move about during praise and worship.
- Take the longest route through the grocery store.
- Do things you like to do (walk, swim, play a sport, join a sports league, hike, camp).
- Take up gardening.
- Do physical labor.
- Wash your car by hand.
- Do housework.
- Add extra movement wherever and whenever you can!

You can add physical activity throughout your day. It doesn't have to be all at once—every minute adds up. Even if you are confined to a chair, you can still be physically active. While sitting down, you can do a modified version of any activity you can do standing up. For instance, you can dance, march, or even do jumping jacks from your chair.

God gave us arms and legs, the sensations of pleasure and fun, and creative ability to enjoy and live life to the fullest! We cannot enjoy our lives if we are overweight, sick, and sluggish. We must use everything the good Lord put at our disposal for our enjoyment if we are going to live the kind of overflowing life He desires for us to live.

How will you choose to continue to live? Will it be a fulfilled life of radical joy and full-blown ecstasy or an unfulfilled life of limited pleasure? Satan, your archenemy, would have you choose the latter. "The thief comes only in order to steal and kill and destroy. I came that they may have and enjoy life, and have it in abundance (to the full, till it overflows)" (John 10:10 AMP).

Call to Action

1. In what ways would exercise improve your health?
2. How much physical activity are you currently getting each day?
3. What is one way you can increase your physical activity?
4. What activities do you think God would have you begin?
5. What action is God prompting you to take?

Lord, I thank You for giving me ability. Please help me to use it in a way that will bring You glory and cause You to be pleased with me. Forgive me for not doing all I am able to do. Change my desires to what pleases You. In Jesus' name I pray. Amen.

Strategy Two

BE DEVOTED AND
CONSECRATED TO GOD

Chapter 6

SET APART FOR GOD

I WANT MY life to be set apart for God's use. Each day, I pray, "Breathe on me and let me think Your thoughts, see with Your eyes, hear Your voice, speak Your words, feel Your feelings, and do Your deeds." I get quite upset with myself when I fall short, which I do every day—many times! I know I'm never going to be perfect, at least not this side of heaven, but it doesn't stop me from wanting to be.

Every day, I commit some sort of sin. I sometimes say mean things to my husband, think bad thoughts, get angry and hold on to it for days, pleasure myself with foods I shouldn't eat, and the list goes on. Like Paul in Romans 7, the things I want to do, I don't always do, and the things I don't want to do, I sometimes find myself doing. Although sin is a persistent foe, it is not the victor! I will continue to press toward the mark of holiness, because there is victory over sin and no condemnation through Jesus Christ.

> But thanks be to God, Who gives us the victory [making us conquerors] through our Lord Jesus Christ.
> —1 Corinthians 15:57 AMP

BE HOLY

We're going to sin. We are descendants of Adam, and sin entered into the world through him, so there is no way around it. But God sent His Son, Jesus Christ, into the world so we could be justified and made righteous through Him. And because we (those who have accepted Jesus Christ as their personal Savior) are made righteous through Him, we should want to live holy lives. Having a propensity to sin doesn't give us a license to do so. God requires us to walk uprightly before Him. One way we can do this is by living lives that are holy.

Romans 12:1 in the Amplified Bible reads, "I appeal to you therefore, brethren, and beg of you in view of [all] the mercies of God, to make a decisive dedication of your bodies [presenting all your members and faculties] as a living sacrifice, holy (devoted, consecrated) and well pleasing to God, which is your reasonable (rational, intelligent) service and spiritual worship." Notice that we are to present our bodies as "holy" to God. According to the *Noah Webster 1828 American Dictionary of the English Language*, "holy" means

> Properly, whole, entire, or perfect, in a moral sense. Hence, pure in heart, temper or dispositions; free from sin and sinful affections. Applied to the Supreme Being, *holy* signifies perfectly pure, immaculate and complete in moral character; and man is more or less *holy*, as his heart is more or less sanctified, or purified from evil dispositions. We call a man *holy*, when his heart is conformed in some degree to the image of God, and his life is regulated by the divine precepts. Hence, *holy* is used as nearly synonymous with good, pious, godly.[1]

Using this definition as a base, there are several facets to note regarding the word *holy*. First, to be holy is to be "proper, whole, or entire in a moral sense." If we learn and obey biblical guidelines—have self-control, resist temptation, and don't give in to the lusts of the flesh—we will know the difference between right and wrong and be wholly proper in our conduct.

Second, to be holy means to be "pure in heart, temper or dispositions." In this sense, to be holy is to have a heart that is sincere and undivided toward God and to keep our minds, feelings, and natural tendencies fully directed toward Him.

Third, to be holy involves being "free from sin and sinful affections." If we do not lend ourselves regularly to sinful behavior but are striving for godly living—and if our hearts aren't drawn to the things and ways of the world—then we are holy.

Fourth, it is apparent that there is a difference between God as holy and people as holy. God is holy in a perfectly pure sense. People are holy if their hearts are sanctified, made holy and clean, through accepting Jesus Christ as Savior. Also, their hearts are free from a natural tendency toward evil because Jesus is Lord of their lives.

Last, according to Webster's definition, a person is holy "when his heart is conformed in some degree to the image of God, and his life is regulated by the divine precepts." This ties together my previous four points. If our lives are regulated by the Word of God, our hearts are devoted to God, and our natural tendency is toward good, then we are holy!

According to the *Student Bible Dictionary*, "holy" means "persons, places, or things set apart for use by God (Deut. 7:6). All holiness originates with God, and all Christians are called to live a holy life—a life like God wants you to live (Lev. 21:8; 1 Thess. 3:13–4:1; 1 Peter 2:9)."[2]

This definition simplifies my previous points. Christians are called to *completely* dedicate their lives to God's use, and doing so makes us holy.

HOLY DEVOTION

To get a clearer picture of what it means to dedicate our bodies as holy to God, let's dig a little deeper into what it means to be holy. In Romans 12:1 the Amplified Bible expands "holy" to also mean being devoted and consecrated.

Webster's 1828 dictionary defines "devoted" as "solemnly set apart or dedicated; consecrated; addicted; given up; doomed; consigned" and *consecrated* as "separated from a common to a sacred use; devoted or dedicated to the service and worship of God; made venerable." In these definitions, I am drawn to the words "addicted" and "consigned." They convey my personal feelings. I am addicted to Jesus! I need more and more of Him in my life, and I just can't seem to get enough. Nothing else can completely satisfy me or the cravings in my soul. Since Jesus is Lord of my life, my present and future are *consigned* to the Lord for His keeping and His management, to use as He sees fit.

I know that being devoted to Him is the best place to be. Being devoted to God, in the form of being addicted and consigned to Him, means we are directed *by* God, resigned *to* Him, and living *for* Him.

HOLY CONSECRATION

To be holy, in reference to being consecrated, means our lives are set apart for God's use. If our lives are consecrated, they will be dedicated to serving Him, following His leading, and doing His will. In other words, we will not live to please others or ourselves. Everything we do—whether we eat, sleep, work, or play—will be dedicated to Him as acts of worship for His honor and glory.

In summary, we are holy, devoted, and consecrated to God if our hearts, minds, and lives are set apart for His use. The *Jamieson, Fausset, and Brown Commentary on the Whole Bible* endorses what I've said in this chapter: "Believers, yielding themselves to God as those that are alive from the dead, and their members as instruments of righteousness unto God, are, in His estimation, not ritually but really holy."[3]

Call to Action

1. In what ways does your life show that you are holy?
2. How does your life show you are devoted and consecrated to God?
3. How much of your life is set apart (devoted) for God's use? Your own use? Others' use?
4. Evaluate your heart, temper, and tendencies. What needs to be changed?
5. What action is God prompting you to take?

Lord, thank You so much for making it possible for me to be holy and regarding me as holy in spite of my sinful nature. Please help me to give my life completely and wholly to You for Your use. Help me find pleasure in living for You and doing everything I can to bring You glory. In Jesus' name I pray. Amen.

Chapter 7

BE GOD'S WITNESS

NOW THAT I'VE lost a significant amount of weight, people are notic-ing, and I am receiving lots of compliments. People are actually stopping me and asking, "What are you doing?" This is when I get to share a little about Romans 12:1–2 and the difference practicing this scripture has made in my life. I'm glad to be a living, breathing example of what is good and godly. I feel honored when people tell me I have helped them think differently about food and that they too are changing their ways so they can be holy, ac-ceptable, and pleasing to God. However, I feel a sense of responsibility when they say, "I'm watching you!" They're bound to notice that I still let my flesh rule sometimes. It's only by God's grace that I live for Him.

People have commented that they've noticed I've maintained my weight loss. I appreciate their comments, but my weight has fluctuated repeatedly—even during this time of seeking to live out Romans 12:1–2. Knowing people are watching me feels like a lot of pressure. I know, however, that I can't focus on what people think about me, nor can I live to please them. Instead, I need to live in a way that is true to my God and to myself. I want to live godly and not just act godly!

"You will be my witnesses, telling people about me everywhere—in Jerusalem, throughout Judea, in Samaria, and to the ends of the earth."

—Acts 1:8 NLT

41

REPRESENT JESUS

Immediately after Jesus spoke those words from Acts 1 to His disciples, He was taken up to heaven, disappearing from their sight. The disciples were henceforth His witnesses (once they were equipped with the power of the Holy Spirit) since, at that point, Jesus no longer lived on the earth in bodily form to bear witness to himself (see Mark 16:19–20, Luke 24:50–53, Acts 1:1–5).

To what were the disciples to be witnesses? They were to testify about the things they learned, heard, and saw while they were with Jesus. We are to do the same thing. We are to bear witness to the things we learn, hear, and see from God during the time we spend with Him studying, praying, meditating, and attending church. The things we learn about Him should be evident in the way we live.

We are to sleep, eat, work, and execute everyday life in a godly way. For example, we should get enough sleep each night so we aren't tired and cranky and unable to diligently perform our daily responsibilities. If we lack energy and are unable to focus due to a shortage of rest—either from taking on too much or not getting adequate sleep—we have done a disservice to ourselves and those whom we serve. Jesus frequently retreated to rest, and we never read about Him being fatigued, cranky, or unable to keep up with the day's demands.

We should also represent Him in the way we eat. We ought to eat foods that give us energy and help us feel good, not sluggish or unwell. When we feel well, we perform better and have a positive disposition. It behooves us to avoid undereating, overeating, and unhealthy eating. These habits do not make us feel good, and they hamper our energy and ability. We never read that Jesus ate improperly or lacked self-control. Rather, we read about His forty-day fast, which tells us He had power over His flesh as far as food was concerned.

Being God's witness isn't something to do only when others are looking. We need to live every day in a way that demonstrates His presence, rule, and effect in our lives. When people look at us, they should be able to see Jesus Christ in us—His love, forgiveness, grace, mercy, goodness, patience, kindness, and self-control. In everything we do, we should reflect Christ as His "living" witnesses.

BE SELF-CONTROLLED

Being a living witness is not easy. My flesh wants nothing to do with God and wants only gratification. My spirit, on the other hand, deeply desires to do God's will and to completely resist temptation. My flesh yells for cupcakes, cookies, and other unhealthy foods. It couldn't care less about how my body feels or the health risks and weight gain from eating these foods. In spite of the battle raging inside me, I am called to stand firm against my flesh and to yield to the Spirit—and so are you!

One day a little over ten years ago, I drove to my teaching job at an elementary school, and my kids were with me because they attended the school where I taught. A couple of blocks from the school, they must have done something that infuriated me, because although they were in the back seat, I managed to fuss, drive, and swat them at the same time! When I got to work, another teacher joked about how my kids must have been acting up because of how I was swinging at them. Even though I laughed and joked with her, I was embarrassed; I never wanted anyone to see me behave that way. In this act, I bore witness to the fact that God hadn't yet worked self-control in me.

Today, I am grateful to bear witness to having self-control (my children like it too). There are still areas that need work, but I have much more self-control than I had ten years ago. Thank God!

As far as my eating is concerned, I am glad God convicted me in a way that led to my repentance and commitment to be a better witness for Him. How could I teach others about health and wellness when I looked unhealthy and unwell? How could I talk about living a life set apart for God when my weight testified that something else had control of me? I knew I couldn't be an effective witness for Christ as long as my outside body didn't match my inside spirit. I needed to give my eating and exercise habits to the Lord. I had to subdue my flesh rather than allowing my flesh to enslave me (1 Cor. 9:27).

This was, and still is, no easy task. But God has given me big dreams, and I've asked Him for many things, none of which can happen if I'm not free to move in the mighty power of His Spirit.

BE AN EXAMPLE

The main reason we are to be living witnesses is so others can come to know Jesus Christ. People's hearts are won to Jesus by what they see in the lives of His followers. I have a friend who grew up in a physically and sexually abusive home, yet she overcame the effects of it through the power of Jesus Christ. She has a loving relationship with her husband. She is raising her children in a loving home. She also serves those in her community, showering love on those around her. Seeing her in action makes me want to do better and love more. I know that the God she believes in has helped her live and love differently than what she experienced as a child. Her example has helped me with similar issues.

Another friend shared her financial hardships that resulted when her husband was laid off. She was struggling and asked me for prayer and moral support. Every Sunday, I watched her come to church with a smile on her face, love in her heart, and a gentle spirit toward others. Her demeanor did not reflect her struggles. Her faith in the Lord helped her live in peace despite her circumstances. Her example has motivated me to seek God for ways to help me move though my problems gracefully too.

Whatever the Lord has taught you will be evident in your life. If He has taught you how to love, people will notice the love you extend to others. If He has taught you forgiveness, you will be viewed as a person who forgives graciously. If He has taught you self-discipline and self-control, it will be evident in your behavior. The opposite is also true: if you have not learned to love, forgive, or have self-control, people will see that as well. If you do not truly know Christ, that too will be evident in the way you live.

PEOPLE ARE WATCHING YOU

At the beginning of the chapter, I mentioned knowing others are watching me feels like a lot of pressure to live up to. As a recovering people pleaser, I must remind myself I am not called to please people, but to please God. The greatest commandment is to love the Lord with all our hearts. If we love God, which pleases Him, and people end up pleased in the process, that's a bonus! It's impossible to go wrong if our focus is on pleasing God, which is why we don't need to worry about what others think of us. God is our Creator, and our eternal destiny is in His hands and not in the hands of people.

We can't control whether people observe our lives and make judgments about us. We can, however, live true to our beliefs and love God with our whole hearts. This relieves the pressure we put on ourselves of having to pretend to be something we are not. Whatever we believe will be a natural part of our lives.

We must ask ourselves what and whom we want to bear witness to. If we want to bear witness to righteousness and holiness, our actions, attitudes, and beliefs will reflect that, and others will be able to tell. If we want to bear witness to Christ, then others will see Him in us and be drawn to Him. This doesn't mean we will behave perfectly in every situation. It does, however, mean that our natural tendency and typical behavior will be a testimony to the Lord Jesus Christ and to righteous living.

Like it or not, we are witnesses. We are either witnesses for Christ or against Him. Whether you are alone in the privacy of your home, in the car with your mate, or in the mall with strangers, how you live and what you do is a testimony of good or evil to those (including God and the enemy) who are in your midst.

Call to Action

1. In what ways are you a living witness for Christ?
2. What things do you need to change to be a greater witness for Him?
3. What things are you willing to change?
4. What action is God prompting you to take?

Lord, You have called me to be Your witness here on earth, which is no easy task. Please fill me with a fresh supply of Your Spirit and enable me to behave in a way that is pleasing to You. Help me, Lord, to do everything I can to draw others to You. In Jesus' name I pray. Amen.

Chapter 8

KEEP YOUR FOCUS ON GOD

RECENTLY I COMPLETED a twenty-one-day fast for the purpose of gaining more self-control. I felt as if, once again, my flesh was dictating to me how to live. I craved more sweets and gave in to those cravings. I also watched more TV as a way to zone out from the hard issues in my life. In an effort to get hold of my flesh and let it know who's boss, I gave up sweets and TV for twenty-one days. In choosing to forgo my fleshly desires, I hoped to be filled with the overcoming power of the Spirit and to gain control over my flesh.

Getting through the twenty-one days became more difficult as the days passed. My flesh started bucking like a wild bull awaiting freedom from its holding pen. At the end of the three weeks, I came out of the gate eager to devour numerous sweets! I didn't, however, allow myself to eat all the things I had fantasized about, because I knew if I did, my flesh would continue to rule, which would defeat the whole purpose of the fast.

Weeks after the fast, I still struggled to keep my focus off all the yummy desserts I wanted to eat. I desperately needed God's help! Even now, I must set my gaze on God so I can overcome this extremely challenging time. If I keep my focus on Him, I know I will be successful in ruling over my flesh rather than letting it rule over me. Thank goodness my confidence is in the God who is in me and not in myself alone.

"Have faith in the LORD your God and you will be upheld … and you will be successful."

—2 Chronicles 20:20 NIV

FOCUS ON RIGHT THINGS

Second Chronicles 20:20 is one of my favorite Scripture verses. Because the chapter and verse is found at "20:20," it makes me think of having 20/20 vision. In this case, having 20/20 vision means I am able to see things clearly and put God's truth into focus. This verse regrounds me in the truth that if I have faith in God, I can handle whatever comes and I will be absolutely successful in the outcome.

The same is true for you. Maintaining victory over fleshly desires may be a struggle for you, but remember that they are no match for God! He overcame everything, and if He lives in you, you are able to overcome all fleshly desires—food, drugs, sex, alcohol, whatever. Keeping your focus on God will help you win.

Keeping your focus on God is not easy because your body and soul (mind, will, and emotions) want only things that bring pleasure and comfort, which are typically not in sync with the Spirit. Your body and soul want immediate gratification regardless of the negative consequences. Your spirit, on the other hand, wants what is pleasing to God. Your body may say, "Give me all the junk food my stomach can hold!" Your spirit, however, says, "Your body is the temple of God. Avoid things that will defile it and take in things that will bless it."

FINE-TUNE YOUR WEAPONS

Three simple ways to keep your focus on God throughout the day are to pray, recite Scripture, and give thanks. During challenging times, however, these may not be enough. You may need to sharpen your prayers, scriptures, and thanksgiving on specific things related to your current struggle. For example, if your current struggle has to do with not giving in to things your body craves, you need to focus on specific tasks that guarantee victory in this particular area. With certain struggles, a general focus on God is not enough. You may need to fine-tune your weapons and use direct-hitting missiles instead.

While writing this chapter, I implemented a laser-focus tactic because my usual focusing practices were not doing the job in helping me overcome my cravings for sweets. I found a packet of Scripture verses I had compiled titled "Scriptures for Losing Weight God's Way" and began to use them to help me in this battle. For each verse, I used a system of *recite*, *memorize*, *pray*, and *give thanks*.

The first was Acts 24:16 (AMP): "Therefore I always exercise and discipline myself [mortifying my body, deadening my carnal affections, bodily appetites, and worldly desires, endeavoring in all respects] to have a clear (unshaken, blameless) conscience, void of offense toward God and toward men."

I recited this scripture throughout the day and worked to memorize it. I also prayed using this scripture. Lastly, I thanked God this scripture will come to pass in my life. I sometimes included a combination of prayer and thanksgiving as I recited the scripture by personalizing it like this: "Lord, I thank You that I always exercise and discipline myself. Thank You that I mortify my body and deaden my carnal affections, bodily appetites, and worldly desires. Thank You that I strive to obey You regarding my affections, appetites, and desires. I am so grateful I have a clear, unshaken, and blameless conscience that is void of offense toward You, people, and myself. Amen."

I have found this method of turning Scripture into a prayer of thanksgiving effective for a variety of reasons. It uses God's Word, which cannot be denied; as it is spoken, it works through the supernatural realm manifesting itself in the natural realm; and it puts thoughts into proper alignment, correcting improper attitudes and causing actions and behaviors to line up with the Word of God. Speaking God's Word is a guarantee of victory! After all, Isaiah 55:11 (KJV) says, "So shall my word be that goeth forth out of my mouth: it shall not return unto me void, but it shall accomplish that which I please, and it shall prosper in the thing whereto I sent it."

TAKE YOUR THOUGHTS CAPTIVE

Another way to keep your focus on God is by taking your thoughts captive. Second Corinthians 10:5 says, "We take captive every thought to make it obedient to Christ." To capture something means to take it prisoner. We are to take captive those thoughts that do not line up with God's Word. Lock them up the way you would an unpardoned criminal. Prisoners are not allowed to roam freely but are told what to do and when to do it. They've been stripped of the rights law-abiding citizens enjoy. Ungodly thoughts should also be denied the right to roam freely in your mind. As soon as they escape, they should be apprehended and immediately taken into custody!

The New Living Translation of the same verse says, "We capture their rebellious thoughts and teach them to obey Christ." We must force rebellious, or natural, thoughts, through strict discipline, to obey Christ the way children are disciplined to obey their parents. It's for the child's good!

When prisoners, or even rebellious children, are allowed to roam freely, those within the vicinity are robbed of peace, security, and freedom. Anything or anyone who does not adhere to rules and authority makes it so that life's normal ease and comfort becomes impossible, causing distress, danger, and various degrees of bondage. Would you allow an escaped prisoner to roam freely in your neighborhood, or a wild child in your home? I don't think so! You would quickly call the police or seek some sort of help to get the lawbreaker bound so you could once again feel safe and live freely. We must do the same with our thoughts.

When negative emotions such as fear, doubt, anger, or bitterness arise, they steal our peace, security, and freedom. Taking captive our thoughts will lead to victory and keep the environment of our body, soul, and spirit peaceful, safe, and free.

FOCUS ON SCRIPTURE

Focusing on Scripture helps us keep our gaze on God. To focus on Scripture includes praying it and thinking deeply about it. The Bible offers help for whatever difficult situation you may find yourself in. To find specific verses for encouragement or motivation, look in a Bible concordance, which can be found in the back of a Bible, online, or as a separate book.

A concordance is an index of the words found in the Bible. It lists portions of all verses containing the particular word (or derivative) you are looking to find. I typically use my concordance to find a verse whose exact location I cannot recall. I am usually able to find it if I know at least one word from the passage.

As you probably know, different Bible translations use different words. Thus, if you are looking for a verse in the King James Version, you may not be able to find the word (or derivative) you are searching for in a New International Version concordance.

You can also look in the subject index, included at the back of many Bibles, to assist you in finding helpful scriptures on specific topics.

READ CHRISTIAN MATERIALS

Reading Christian (not secular) books, periodicals, or articles on your topic of interest will also help to keep your focus on God. Topical books are extremely helpful because usually the author has done an in-depth study of the material and condensed it, making it easier for you to glean information.

PRACTICE SELF-DISCIPLINE

One last way to keep our focus on God is to practice self-discipline. The *New American Webster's Handy College Dictionary* defines "discipline" as "mental and moral training, obedience to rules," and "correction; chastisement."

Mental and moral training comes when we practice mental self-discipline by forbidding our thoughts to roam freely, capturing thoughts that should be bound, and keeping our mind at peace. We learn godly principles and receive moral training by focusing on Scripture and reading Christian materials.

For some, self-discipline in the area of food is a challenge. When thoughts of unhealthy foods pop into your mind, visualize all the negative consequences that will come from eating them (for example, gas, bloating, inflammation, pain, weight gain, and nausea). Once you've exhausted every negative possibility, think about the healthy foods you could eat instead and visualize all the positive benefits you will receive (nourishment for your body and mind, energy, peace, mental clarity, renewed strength, and so forth). It's a scriptural truth and scientific fact that the things you think about affect your actions. In the end, picturing the positive and negative consequences in detail will help you make a better choice. (I say "better" because realistically we won't always make the best choice. For example, it may be best for me to not eat cake at all. On the other hand, if I really want it, a better choice would be limiting myself to a very small piece.)

Practicing self-discipline helps us obey God's commands, found in His Word. God wants what is best for us, and obedience to Him allows us to experience the fully blessed life God intended us to have (see John 10:10 AMP).

Correction and chastisement are a big part of self-discipline, yet we don't hear much about them. And there's a reason for that omission. I must confess I was horrified when I found out that "mortify" in the Amplified Bible's translation of Acts 24:16 means "to humiliate; to subject the body to extreme discipline." What? Humiliate my body? Subject it to *extreme* discipline? This is almost unthinkable! My body likes pleasure and finds great enjoyment in a lack of self-restraint. It loves to eat whatever it wants and delights in lots of fat and sugar. But I must not permit myself to do everything I like, because not everything is beneficial for me (1 Cor. 6:12 NIV).

Humiliating or subjecting our bodies to extreme discipline may seem outrageous, yet Scripture recommends it. First Corinthians 9:27 (AMP) says, "But [like a boxer] I buffet my body [handle it roughly, discipline it by hardships] and subdue it." The New Living Translation reads, "I discipline my body like an athlete, training it to do what it should." Correcting and chastising your body and forcing it to obey God helps you to be victorious. It also makes you fit for Christian service.

FOCUS ON GOD

In summary, keeping our focus on God increases our likelihood of success in every situation we face. We can overcome overeating, alcoholism, addiction, fear, anger, relationship issues, and anything else if we fix our gaze upon God and His Word. We can keep our focus on God by praying, reciting Scripture, and continuously giving thanks. We can also take captive our thoughts, focus on Scripture, read Christian books, and most of all, practice obedience to God.

God has given us keys of victory to everything we will encounter on earth. Jesus said, "I will give you the keys of the kingdom of heaven; whatever you bind on earth will be bound in heaven, and whatever you loose on earth will be loosed in heaven" (Matt. 16:19 NIV). We are victorious! With God, we win! "But thanks be to God! He gives us the victory through our Lord Jesus Christ" (1 Cor. 15:57 NIV).

Call to Action

1. Name at least one obstacle that is keeping you from focusing on God.
2. What can you do to remove that obstacle?
3. Identify a passage of Scripture that will help you in your biggest area of difficulty.
4. What action is God prompting you to take?

Lord, please help me to set my gaze on You. Please help me realize just how much I need You. I can do nothing without You. Thank You for being my adequacy in all things. Most of all, thank You for dying and making it possible for Your Holy Spirit to live in me so I can be victorious in every situation. In Jesus' name I pray. Amen.

Strategy Three

GIVE GOD YOUR REASONABLE SERVICE

Chapter 9

WELL-PLEASING SERVICE

I'VE ALWAYS BEEN *a good employee and provided my employer with excellent service. I show up on time, get along with others, am self-motivated, rarely take off, put in extra time when I'm at home regardless of whether I get paid or not, and go well above the call of duty.*

With all of my positive qualities as an employee, there is one area where I've been repeatedly convicted—taking advantage of office supplies. At my worst, I've gone from getting my husband to take every imaginable office supply from his job to furnish my home office, to a few months ago when I left my last job, making sure I went home with a couple of almost-new Post-it® pads. A voice inside me told me to leave them, but I ignored the voice and kept the pads. To some, this may not seem like a big deal, but I know my behavior was wrong. Buying my own note pads would have been the right thing to do.

The Holy Spirit convicted me about taking those pads because taking office supplies isn't holy, isn't pleasing to God, and isn't acceptable. I conformed to the world's way of doing things, which says it's OK to take office supplies to use at home if you need them. (Had my supervisor given me the OK to take them, I wouldn't have been out of line with Romans 12:1–2.)

Taking office supplies, making personal copies, extending breaks or lunchtimes, slacking in productivity, surfing the Internet, making personal phone calls, texting, and so on is wrong if those activities have nothing to do with serving your employer. In everything we do, we must work as if we are serving God. In order to give God our reasonable service, we must do everything—publicly and privately—in a way that brings honor and glory to Him.

> Servants (slaves), be obedient to those who are your physical masters, having respect for them and eager concern to please them, in singleness of motive and with all your heart, as [service] to Christ [Himself]—Not in the way of eye-service [as if they were watching you] and only to please men, but as servants (slaves) of Christ, doing the will of God heartily and with your whole soul; Rendering service readily with goodwill, as to the Lord and not to men.
>
> —Ephesians 6:5–7 AMP

SERVING YOUR EMPLOYER

Most people act as if taking office supplies is a privilege that comes with the job. I beg to differ. If our employers haven't specifically given the OK to take supplies home, it's wrong. Just because others do so doesn't make it right. A storage area filled with supplies (or being able to order them at our leisure) does not give us the right to get whatever we need for personal use.

As taking office supplies is wrong, so is using our jobs as a means to gain personal privileges. Work schedules, breaks, expectations, and benefits are usually made clear upon hire, and as employees we are required to abide by the terms to which we agreed. If extending breaks, arriving late, leaving early, making personal phone calls, texting, surfing the Internet, or using office supplies for personal purposes dishonors God in any way, don't do it.

We employees are to serve our employers. They hire us for service. As Christians our job is to obey instructions, exceed expectations, and seek to please our employers as we would Christ. In Ephesians 6:5–7, we are commanded to obey our masters (those in authority over us) and serve them respectfully and with integrity, in and out of their sight, as if Jesus were our supervisor.

I believe if we viewed Jesus as our literal supervisor, we would behave very differently on the job. The Lord is omnipresent and omniscient. This means He is everywhere, and He knows everything we do (and don't do). One day we will each stand before God and give an account for everything we've done. Our eternal rewards will be based on our life's deeds (2 Cor. 5:10; Rev. 22:12). Keeping eternity in mind will influence true Christians to do the right thing.

SERVING GOD

God is the ultimate boss, and everyone, including our employers, operates under His authority. It behooves us to give Him our best service since He sees everything we do and rewards us according to our works.

In Romans 12:1, we are commanded to present our bodies—which includes everything we do—to God in a way that is holy, acceptable, and yields reasonable service. As I pondered the part of this verse that reads "present your bodies a living sacrifice, holy, acceptable unto God, which is your reasonable service (KJV)," the word *living* jumped out at me in a way it never had before. I thought of a living sacrifice as one that is alive—the opposite of dead—and being full of life. Old Testament sacrifices involved killing living creatures. I don't recall reading or hearing about a sacrifice in which the creature did not die.

It wasn't until Jesus came that *life* was associated with a sacrifice. Jesus became the ultimate sacrifice—the perfect, spotless Lamb of God. He allowed himself to be put to death on the cross for our sins, and three days later He came back to life. He was the final sacrifice needed to atone for the sins of the world.

It is clear Jesus fulfilled the command in the previously mentioned portion of Romans 12:1. He willingly presented His body as the ultimate living sacrifice that was fully holy and completely acceptable to God, as a reasonable service for mankind, fulfilling the sacrificial requirements for our sins. Jesus gave up His divine position in heaven to come to earth in human form to serve humankind by affording everyone who believes on Him the opportunity to obtain everlasting life!

We are to follow Jesus' example of giving up personal pleasure and position for the overall good of others. Like Jesus, we are to pursue things that contribute to life, and we are to cease things that beckon death. We are to do things that draw others to Christ and forgo things that pull others away from Him.

For the majority of my life, I did not follow Jesus' example of giving up personal pleasure in regard to eating. I pursued fat- and sugar-laden delights, shortening my life span and hurrying death. In addition, my behavior neglected to draw others to the saving knowledge of Christ—to a new restaurant maybe, but God, no. I believe my eating habits and passion for food incited others to indulge in self-gratification and the fulfillment of pleasure regardless of the cost.

As *living* sacrifices, we are to live in ways that draw people to God. This requires "reasonable service." The Amplified Bible says, "to make a decisive dedication of your bodies [presenting all your members and faculties] as a living sacrifice, holy (devoted, consecrated) and well pleasing to God, which is your reasonable (rational, intelligent) service and spiritual worship."

I learn several things from this translation. First of all, we are to make a decisive dedication to present our bodies as *living* sacrifices. This means we make a resolute decision to devote the use of every single part of our bodies (its members) and our mental capacity and aptitude (its faculties) to God. In other words, whatever we do with our bodies and whatever we allow ourselves to think should somehow serve God. Second, we should live in a way that leads others to give their lives to Christ. Third, the bodies we present to God are to be holy and well pleasing. Profane, immoral, self-seeking, and indulgent behaviors are not holy or pleasing to God. Only a life of sacrifice is *reasonable service*. The Amplified Bible describes *reasonable* as "rational and intelligent." This means to live in a way that demonstrates sound spiritual judgment and an understanding of God's will.

As followers of Christ, we are to exemplify Him, to display His qualities. Jesus always gave His very best, demonstrated excellence, and exhibited integrity in the way He lived and in the works He did. We are to do the same.

REASONABLE SERVICE

Reasonable service includes giving our best to everything we do. This is not limited to what we do for income. We are called to be the best Christians (followers of Christ) possible. We are to serve at home, work, church, and in the community the best way we can, rendering our best effort. Whether we are in public or private, or operating in our vocation or avocation, our actions, attitudes, and behaviors should be our best representation of Christ.

Reasonable service includes doing tasks with excellence and care. Our performance should involve a high output of work, of superior quality with minimal waste. Demonstrating mediocrity, slothfulness, and wastefulness are not giving God reasonable service.

Reasonable service also includes exhibiting integrity. This means we adhere to the moral principles established by God. We are honest and tell the truth even if it hurts, does not benefit us, or is difficult to do. We demonstrate good judgment and godly values in our activities, decisions, and deeds. We are completely trustworthy.

LACKING REASONABLE SERVICE

December 31, 2009, God convicted me of not giving Him my reasonable service. That night, as I lay on the altar, I could see that I hadn't given Him my very best, because my unhealthy eating habits had caused physical limitations and ailments. I didn't have the energy or stamina to praise God very long because I was overweight and out of shape. I became easily winded performing everyday tasks involving movement. Recent medical tests had revealed my cholesterol, blood pressure, blood-sugar levels, and weight were either borderline, moderately high, or high. Self-indulgent eating was the cause.

I felt conviction because I had not demonstrated excellence as far as physical activity was concerned. I chose not to exercise and to move my body very little. Instead of using the time I had available for physical activity, I squandered it sitting, lying around, and eating. Opting for laziness, I disregarded the muscles, bones, and strong body God had given me.

Furthermore, I neglected to be excellent in my eating. I mostly made mediocre or poor food choices and frequently overate. For the most part, I ignored everything I knew about healthy eating in order to fulfill personal food desires and please my flesh.

I was also convicted that I had not exhibited integrity. God requires us to have self-control, even in our eating; I did not. He requires us to relinquish things that cause others to sin; I dragged others into my food escapades. He requires us to be aboveboard about the things we do; I often sneaked food and made sure I got the biggest or best portion. God requires us to demonstrate good judgment regarding our activities, decisions, and deeds; I chose to eat things that jeopardized my health, made me feel bad, and added extra weight.

NEVER GIVE UP

I continue to evaluate my reasonable service, and I still have plenty of room for improvement. On one hand I'm embarrassed and sad. On the other hand, I am comforted, hopeful, and extremely grateful because of God's mercy and grace. Not because His mercy and grace give me a license to continue sinning, but because they motivate me to keep striving toward the mark of giving God my reasonable service even when I fail.

Giving God our reasonable service requires *sacrifice*. We must sacrifice our wills and personal desires for God's will and His desires. We must put to death (forget about) what we want and allow what God wants to live in and through us. This is not always fun or easy to do, which is why it's called sacrifice!

Being a living sacrifice is a Christian's reasonable service. Along with drawing others to God, exemplifying Christ, giving our best in everything we do, and doing things with excellence, our reasonable service also includes continually giving God praise, doing good to others, and obeying authority. "Through Jesus, therefore, let us continually offer to God a sacrifice of praise—the fruit of lips that confess his name. And do not forget to do good and to share with others, for with such sacrifices God is pleased. Obey your leaders and submit to their authority. They keep watch over you as men who must give an account. Obey them so that their work will be a joy, not a burden, for that would be of no advantage to you" (Heb. 13:15–17 NIV).

Sacrifices of praise are not merely verbal expressions of honor but also are attitudes and actions that demonstrate honor. (We'll talk more about this in a later chapter.) Doing good means more than sharing or giving to others. It includes working for the common good, being kind, and helping those in need.

Reasonable service is synonymous with true worship. Worshiping God in the way we live is our reasonable service; and our reasonable service involves living a life of worship. According to a *TNIV Study Bible* note, our reasonable service is not "merely ritual activity but the involvement of heart, mind and will in worship and obedient service."

Let's sharpen our spiritual sensitivities so we do not justify sin and are not comfortable with it. Let's rid ourselves of the world's ways and things that are not acceptable and pleasing to God. Let's strive to give Him our true worship and reasonable service.

Call to Action

1. If God were to evaluate your performance, how pleased would He be with your work?
2. What two areas would receive the worst critique?
3. What can you do to receive a better critique?
4. What specifically does "give God your very best" mean to you?
5. What action is God prompting you to take?

Lord, please forgive me for not giving You my best in everything I do. Please help me to resist the temptation of having my own way. Cleanse me so I operate in excellence and integrity in everything I do. Bless me to give You my reasonable service, which is true worship. Help me honor You in this way. In Jesus' name I pray. Amen.

Chapter 10

DEEPER WORSHIP

WORSHIP. IT MEANS more than clapping, lifting hands, or bowing down during the praise-and-worship portion of a church service. About seven years ago, I discovered more of what it means. A year ago, I learned even more. Even though I understand there is a depth to worship, I often fall back into my old thinking, which still finds the rudimentary actions of worship enough.

What makes it so much easier to believe I'm giving God worship through a simple hand clap or lifting my hands? I think it's because these actions don't require much effort. As a matter of fact, the only "sacrifice" required is when I clap my hands when I don't feel like it, force myself to keep my arms raised when they are tired, or risk embarrassment and speak words of adoration aloud to God when others around me are quiet.

God has done so much for me that He is worth more than these elementary forms of worship. Not only that, He expects more from His children. He requires the totality of worship, which I don't always want to give. I don't give Him all my worship because it's hard, and an easy life is more palatable.

Seeking to live an easy life is unacceptable for God's children, because He requires more from us. In addition to this, He deserves more from us as His servants. Since He created us, giving Him what He wants is the least we can do.

"But an hour is coming, and now is, when the true worshipers will worship the Father in spirit and truth; for such people the Father seeks to be His worshipers."

—John 4:23 NASB

JOURNEY TO WORSHIP

Growing up, I attended soul-filled, fire-and-brimstone-preaching Baptist churches. I had a couple of brief stints at two different reserved, power-of-thought-teaching Unity churches. At these churches, we learned about God and sang songs about Him, yet I don't recall ever hearing "Worship God."

I first heard "Worship God" at the age of sixteen when I went to an Assemblies of God church with my friend and her mother. I recall seeing emotionally engrossed people with their hands lifted up and eyes closed. I heard professions like "We worship You, O God" and quiet whispers of "I worship You, Lord" and "I honor You." The pastor repeatedly proclaimed, "Worship Him! Worship Him!" A couple of times, he passionately ordered, "Lift up your hands and worship Him!" Since I had never been directed to worship God before, I copied those around me and lifted my arms toward heaven.

Over the years, I graduated from absentmindedly singing and timidly lifting my hands to soulfully bellowing praise songs, sincerely lifting and waving my hands, reverently bowing my head, and shamelessly getting down on my knees. I thought these actions signified worshiping God. Little did I know *true* worship means so much more.

About seven years ago, I studied what worship means. I was surprised to learn that worship is not just an outward expression. I discovered that not only does it include actions that express praise, love, and appreciation for God, but it also includes an *attitude* that expresses praise, love, and appreciation for God. Additionally, worship is expressed through obedience to God (Deut. 10:12–13).

ATTITUDE CHANGES

At the time of this discovery, I had a major problem with my attitude. It was extremely negative. I didn't believe God truly loved me. I didn't think I was worth loving, for that matter. I struggled to believe God was good and not out to punish me. I expected the worst and didn't believe for the best. I ruminated on bad things that happened to me and constantly entertained self-defeating thoughts. My negative attitude affected every area of my life. Food addiction and emotional eating became a sordid escape.

My attitude has changed drastically since then, and it continues to change as I study God's Word and learn the truth about Him. From my studies, I have learned God actually is good and doesn't seek to hurt me (Ps. 84:11; Rom. 8:28). I learned He wants what is best for me, and since only He is all wise, only He knows what that is (Rom. 11:33–36). I began to understand and accept that He loves me and isn't out to punish me (Ps. 103:8–13; John 3:16–17). I changed my thinking, began focusing on the positive side of things, and started speaking good things over my life (Prov. 23:7; Phil. 4:8). Everything in my life changed for the better, including my eating.

Before this change took place, I discovered I used food as a substitute for seeking and trusting in God. I ate to soothe *all* my emotions—happy or sad, good or bad—rather than seek gratification from God. When I had a problem, the first thing I turned to was food, rather than praying or finding an answer in the Bible. When I felt lonely or needed support, I turned to food. *Food*, not God, was my comforter, problem solver, and best friend.

Studying the Bible helped me change my overall attitude and behavior toward food and put them in the proper place. Food had become my idol. I worshiped it and not God. Worshiping God instead of food is an ongoing battle because food was my crutch for so long. Now, most of the time, I recognize my old habits of wanting to turn to food instead of God, and I make the choice to turn to Him to meet my needs.

My greatest struggle is worshiping God through obedience. The biggest area of disobedience has to do with food. Even though I have changed, there are still times when I am more obedient to the call of my cravings than to the self-control God requires of me. I'm striving toward complete obedience to God and self-discipline in this area. I want to obey His direction and have self-control in managing my portion sizes, choosing foods that are beneficial for me, staying physically active, and surrendering my will to His.

EXTREME SUBMISSION

God is calling true worshipers to surrender to His authority and will. To truly worship Him, He requires us to yield our power to His power, control, and rule. Eating whatever *I* want, doing whatever *I* please, and thinking whatever *I* desire does not worship God. Though God has given us self-will and personal power, truly worshiping Him requires us to surrender our will and power to Him.

In chapter 1, I gave this definition of worship: "to honor with extravagant love and extreme submission." Submission, as far as eating is concerned, involves seeking the Holy Spirit for guidance about what and what not to eat. It is allowing the Spirit and the Word to dictate what we eat and then honoring God by following His leading. Submission itself is challenging, let alone adding *extreme* submission to the mix. Most of us have trouble complying with submission, so we really need help with extreme submission!

Extreme submission means resisting the urge to eat even a mini cupcake or take a bite of sweets if the Spirit says no. (This is the part I find extremely difficult. I still want small amounts when God says no.) Extreme submission means not having these foods around or even entertaining thoughts about eating them when God has said not to. How is extreme submission possible?

Extreme means "to the greatest degree." If we want to truly worship God, we must yield to Him to the greatest degree possible. This means all our thoughts, actions, and motivations are in line with His. Our wills become all about doing His will. We no longer live separate from Christ, but are so intertwined with Him that His life becomes part of us—His will becomes ours.

In all honesty, I find this difficult, because there are times when I want to do what pleases me more than I want to do what pleases Him.

EXTRAVAGANT LOVE

Love in its truest sense is sacrificial (1 Cor. 13:4–7)—for the good of those we love. If this is true, then extravagant love requires the greatest possible personal sacrifice. Christ demonstrated this type of love for us when He gave His life for us. If we love Him extravagantly, we'll show it by completely surrendering our lives to Him and seeking His will above our own.

I want to grow in my love for Christ so I can demonstrate extravagant love to Him by living in total surrender to Him, always doing His will and never my own. This may seem impossible, but it isn't. Recall Paul in the Bible. He gave up everything that meant anything, and demonstrated true worship to God. He gave up his status and power in order to spread the good news of Jesus Christ (Phil. 3:4–7). He endured many hardships and trials for the sake of the gospel (2 Cor. 11:23–27). He desired to do the will of his Father, and he rejoiced in that. He counted complete surrender to God's will as gain and not loss (Phil. 3:7–8). His life of extreme submission glorified God and won many souls for Christ.

Paul isn't the only example of extravagant love and extreme submission. There are also present-day examples. Mother Teresa demonstrated extravagant love and extreme submission by giving her life to help poor, sick, orphaned, and dying children and people. Corrie ten Boom helped Jews escape the Nazis during World War II, and once imprisoned, taught fellow prisoners about Jesus Christ. After her release, she helped in rehabilitation camps and traveled all over the world telling people about the faithfulness of God.

Last but certainly not least, there's little-known Rev. Frank Williams, pastor of Mount Carmel Missionary Baptist Church, a small congregation in Kansas City, Missouri. He tirelessly and joyously serves God by demonstrating His love and spreading the gospel message to homeless persons, those in hospitals, and those in need. Every day, he cheerfully gives of his life to serve and love people—even those he does not know. I've never met anyone as loving, cheerful, giving, and selfless as he.

These men and women of faith are *true* worshipers. They have yielded their lives to Christ, and they honor Him by demonstrating extravagant love and extreme submission.

TRUE WORSHIP

As we can see from these few examples, truly worshiping God is definitely doable. Not only is it doable, but this is the kind of worship the Father is seeking (John 4:23). Like Paul, Mother Teresa, Corrie ten Boom, and Rev. Frank Williams, we have to make a firm decision to serve God and surrender to His rule and authority rather than to our own pleasure and will.

God has given us free will so we can choose to do whatever we want. We can decide not to worship Him at all, or to give Him partial worship, or to give Him our true worship. If we give Him anything less than true worship, we miss the mark and we sin. When we choose not to worship God with our whole selves—spirit, body, and soul (mind, will, and emotions)—we get off course spiritually, physically, mentally, emotionally, relationally, financially—every way possible.

Continuously living a life of true worship is easier to do than getting out of the messes that arise from getting off track. A sustained life of true worship may seem harder because it requires constantly giving up our will and submitting to God's. In the long run, however, choosing our will over God's invites spiritual separation from Him, physical pain, emotional unrest, relational problems, and a host of other issues.

When I choose to eat in a way that goes against God's will for me, I experience spiritual separation from God, because my disobedience puts a wedge between us. Physically, I experience bodily discomfort in the form of aches, pains, headaches, gas, bloating, and so forth. Mentally, my thinking becomes foggy, and I am unable to concentrate. Emotionally and relationally, too much sugar causes my emotions to get out of whack, and I become irritable and hard to get along with. Financially, I waste money by purchasing unnecessary and unhealthy foods.

When I truly worship God in my eating, I surrender the way I eat to Him and obey His direction. Doing so, my spiritual connection with Him remains intact. Physically, I feel energetic and vibrant. Mentally, my mind is clear and alert, especially to the enemy's schemes. Emotionally, I am stable because I've allowed the Spirit to reign. Relationally, I get along with others because my emotions aren't out of control. Financially, I'm a good steward because I don't waste money on unnecessary food and remedies to correct ailments that arise from disobedient eating.

I long to be a *true* worshiper, worshiping God with extravagant love and extreme submission. I don't want to offer just outward expressions of praise like singing worship songs, lifting my hands, or bowing my head. I want to offer worship that is reflected in godly actions and attitudes, total obedience, and letting God have complete authority and rule over every area of my life. How about you?

Call to Action

1. What habits or attitudes do you need to change to become a true worshiper?
2. Who or what is the ultimate authority figure in your life?
3. In what ways have you moved off course by not giving God your true worship?
4. Identify at least two people (famous or otherwise) who exemplify true worship.
5. What action is God prompting you to take?

Lord, thank You for revealing biblical truths and for teaching me how to grow in You. Help me to become a true worshiper. Forgive me for wanting my will above Yours. Please help me to love You enough to do Your will. Transform my thinking and desires so I prefer Your will above everything else. Bless me to honor You with extravagant love and extreme submission so I may be found holy, acceptable, and pleasing in Your sight. In Jesus' name I pray. Amen.

Chapter 11

SAFETY PRECAUTIONS

*T*HE HOLIDAY SEASON *had arrived. For me, the beginning of October to the first week in January is a time of readily available candies, treats, and excessive celebratory eating. I watched my weight gradually increase over these few months. The pounds went up, up, up—.2, .5, .7, 1.0, 1.5, 2.0—until I had gained a whopping 7.2 pounds! All of the months of saying no, resisting temptation, and exercising to get the weight off slowly slipped down the drain.*

Every day of those three months, I weighed myself and set out to make better choices and do the right thing. I didn't want the holidays to get the best of me, yet I failed. I couldn't seem to get a handle on things. One day, it dawned on me: I was no longer presenting my body as a sacrifice to God. Without realizing it, I had once again conformed to the world's ways and my old thinking. I falsely reasoned I could eat what I wanted and still lose weight by doing X, Y, and Z, which had nothing to do with disciplining my flesh or obeying God.

In mid January, I finally came to my senses. I realized that obeying God and doing His will had to be my focus rather than losing weight if I were going to be successful. I worked on strengthening my spirit and depriving my flesh over the next few months. Focusing on changing the inside of me allowed me to get the outside weight off. I should know by now, after so many setbacks, that I cannot put trust in my flesh because it always lets me down. Thank God I can turn to my Redeemer who's always there to help me out of the pit.

If you think you are standing strong, be careful not to fall. The temptations in your life are no different from what others experience. And God is faithful. He will not allow the temptation to be more than you can stand. When you are tempted, he will show you a way out so that you can endure.

—1 Corinthians 10:12–13 NLT

SAFETY PRECAUTIONS

We implement safety precautions when we do things like wear a seatbelt to lessen bodily harm from an automobile accident, pray over our food to block things that may harm us, tie our shoelaces to avoid tripping, and wash our hands to counteract sickness. These safety precautions don't necessarily stop misfortune from happening, but they greatly reduce their chances, as well as the extent of their damages.

Likewise, we can implement spiritual safety precautions to keep us on track—or help us get back to where we need to be. Everyone gets off course at one time or another. No one will ever be perfect in all areas at all times. This doesn't make us failures—it makes us human. Although we are bound to falter at some point, we don't have to call it quits. We can get back on track and use the guardrails God gave us to limit the extent of possible damage. These guardrails are what I call safety precautions.

I take four precautions every day to help me reach my goal of being found as holy, acceptable, and pleasing to God. These are *prayer, Scripture reading* and *Scripture meditation*, and *weighing daily*.

Prayer

I start my day in prayer because I know there is power in prayer (James 5:16). Prayer draws my attention to God and elevates my thinking to a holy perspective. It opens lines of communication between God and me and gives me an opportunity to bring my concerns to Him. When I take time to listen, it improves my outlook and attitude about things. Prayer is the key to success in every area of life. It invites God in. It also helps me order my day, build proper relationships, garner self-control, stay focused on Him, get protection, and other things too numerous to mention. Prayer helps set in motion everything needed for a triumphant day.

Scripture Reading and Scripture Meditation

Reading and meditating on Scripture are two other important safety precautions. Getting my mind on the right track wins half the battle. Reading Scripture informs me of God's perspective, reveals His truth, and helps turn my wrong thinking into what is right. Meditating on Scripture takes reading to a deeper level. It involves thinking deeply about the Word of God, which counteracts false beliefs, discouragement, and faulty thinking. It helps my thoughts stay on the right track. It gets the truth deep into my spirit. It encourages, builds confidence, gives hope, and leads to improved self-esteem.

Finding the right scriptures and letting the truth sink into the depths of my heart and mind leave me feeling as if I can accomplish anything.

Weighing Daily

Last year, I heard that people who weigh themselves daily are better able to manage their weight. I frowned when I first heard this, because I didn't care to receive a daily reminder about my weight. I didn't like the weekly weight checks some diet plans and programs suggested; I definitely wasn't happy about the thought of more weight checks! I had a scale but rarely weighed myself; the numbers always disappointed me and spoke the truth about my overeating and sedentary lifestyle.

Twice more over the next several months, I heard about the benefits of daily weighing. When I began my Romans 12:1–2 journey of transformation, I asked God to show me the truth about myself because I wanted to be found pleasing in His sight. So I decided to give daily weighing a try. Lo and behold, it worked! I lost about fifteen pounds in about three months.

For me, checking my weight daily limits the likelihood of excessive weight gain. It's easier to lose a small amount of weight than a large amount, and I'm less likely to get depressed or feel overwhelmed. Also, since my weight is fresh in my mind, my subconscious readily kicks in, reminding me when I need to do more activity, make healthier food choices, and better manage portion sizes.

When I rarely weighed myself, I'd be horrified by the amount of weight I had gained when I did get on the scale. I'd fall into depression thinking about the amount of effort, discipline, and deprivation it would take to get the weight off. To deal with my sorrow, I ate to drown the pain and gained even more weight.

Daily weight checks are a safety precaution. They let us know whether we are headed in the right direction or toward destruction. They inform us of hazards before we get miles off course and prevent us from wasting valuable time, energy, and effort.

Note: Hormonal changes, water retention, medication, and other things can influence your weight. Should you decide to implement daily weight checks, be careful not to let your weight become an obsession or idol. Daily weight checks should be viewed only as a safety precaution and not a legalistic ritual.

The Most Important Precautions

Daily prayer and Scripture reading and meditation are the most important of the three safety precautions. They are more important because they help us get hold of our flesh and give us the ability to accomplish the tasks God calls us to accomplish through His strength, might, and power. These precautions are primary because of the specific areas they fortify.

Prayer sets the foundation for how the day will proceed. It charts the course for overcoming problems, helps us fight, and gives us supernatural power that leads to victory.

Science has proven that our brains react to whatever we think about. Brain chemicals are released when we think. Uplifting chemicals are released when we think positively, and depressive ones are released when we think negatively. Reading and meditating on confidence-building scriptures, along with prayer, works in our favor to take us closer to victory.

Scripture reading brings sustenance. It is spiritual food that nourishes and sustains us for whatever we may encounter. Meditation grounds our thinking. It sets our mind on a godly path. It is a spiritual energy vitamin boost. It equips us to be mentally ready for the battles that are sure to come and packs us with mental stamina for the fight.

STRENGTHEN YOUR SPIRITUAL CONDITION

Begin each day with prayer. Start by rendering praise and thanksgiving to God for who He is and what He's done in your life. Petition Him about the activities of the day and ask for His leading, direction, and will to be done. Ask for His guidance regarding vocations and avocations. Ask Him to reveal His purpose and plan for the day. Ask for greater love, commitment, and extreme submission, as well as the grace to do His will. Ask for personal renewal, spiritual insight, wisdom, and discernment. Intercede for family, friends, people, ministries, institutions, and organizations. Ask for His provision (spiritual, mental, emotional, physical, and financial) for whatever the day may bring. Ask for protection and help for any special concerns you may have. Confess your sins and ask for forgiveness.

All this may seem as if will take hours to get through. It's possible, but not necessary. Let the Holy Spirit lead you on what to pray. If you aren't sure of the Holy Sprit's leading, pick out what seems most pressing to you. If nothing is pressing, choose specific concerns to pray about. You can even purchase a devotional book to help you pray. There's no magic formula or right or wrong way to pray. What *is* important is that you spend time praying, because it ushers in help, strength, and power (see James 5:16).

If this still seems like a bit much, pray the Lord's Prayer. Jesus' model for how to pray includes *adoration* (praise for who God is), *submission* (surrender to His authority), *petition and intercession* (requests for your and others' needs), and *confession* (admitting your sins). Be sure to include these aspects when you pray.

Praying to God should not be drudgery or a point on a to-do list. It should be a way of life, as natural and automatic as breathing. Prayer, simply put, is communicating with God.

WHEN PROBLEMS ARISE

Even if safety precautions are in place, problems are bound to arise. When they do, here is a simple four-step method for solving them.

Identify the problem. Clearly pinpoint the root problem.

Implement a solution. Come up with as many solutions as possible. Choose one or two to try—no more than three. (Keep it simple.)

Assess the results. If your plan works, continue. If it doesn't, implement a different solution.

Evaluate your progress. After a period of time, evaluate the situation to see whether or not you have mastered it. If you've resolved the problem, then all is well. If you haven't, keep doing the part that is working, and try another solution on your list. If that doesn't work, look again at what you identified as the root problem; it's possible you identified it incorrectly. Should this be the case, determine the problem and go through the steps again. If you still don't master the problem, ask your family, friends, doctor(s), or other professionals for help.

Here is one way I used this process. Weighing myself daily and seeing the gradual weight gain revealed to me I had a problem. I wanted to eat whatever I desired, regardless of the fat and sugar content. I also loosely monitored portions and hardly engaged in physical activity. Spiritually, I wanted to be free from moral restraint and let my flesh have its way.

Once I identified the problem, I brainstormed solutions: measure my food, make a meal plan in advance, increase physical activity, keep a food and activity log, limit fatty and sugary foods, increase positive self-talk, get an accountability buddy, memorize Scripture.

I decided to (1) complete a food and activity log so I could see exactly what I ate and drank and how much I moved each day; (2) set a food goal to limit sugary food to no more than four servings a week; and (3) set a physical activity goal of at least thirty minutes three times a week. I did this for one month and then evaluated my progress.

These steps helped me lose about two of the seven pounds I had gained, so I decided to implement a new solution to help me lose the remaining five pounds. I continued to complete my food and activity logs and to meet my food and activity goals, since they were working. Then I chose three more things to try: (1) I increased my physical activity to a minimum of three hours per week; (2) I memorized Scripture to help boost my confidence, encourage myself, and foster positive results; and (3) I added positive self-talk. I spoke what I wanted the outcome to be. I made confidence-building statements like "I make good food choices," "I eat right," "I look good and feel good," "I am getting smaller," and "I weigh what God would have me weigh." I did this for another month and then reevaluated.

I lost another pound or two, so I went back to the drawing board. After careful evaluation, I realized I was still eating too many high-fat foods. I also noticed my body was going through a variety of changes that were attributable to my hormones being out of balance.

I set out on a new plan to limit my fat intake and deal with the hormonal imbalances. A week into my new plan, I ended up sick with the flu. The blessing is I lost seven pounds in one week! The downside was, of course, having all the symptoms that go along with having the flu! This knocked off the rest of the weight (and then some, but it's not a viable weight-loss method). I continued with the solutions that worked, even though the holiday weight was gone. I began monitoring my fat intake and taking homeopathic remedies for my hormones, because the fat and hormone problems still needed to be addressed.

I don't take my weight loss for granted. I've learned from experience that just as soon as I *think* I've got everything under control, I could fall (1 Cor. 10:12)! I keep safety precautions in place so I don't risk regaining the weight that took me so long to lose.

I have used these four simple steps for a variety of problems, such as overcoming fear, resolving people conflicts, managing pain, dealing with food challenges, and solving work-related issues. Sometimes problems are taken care of quickly, and other times they are not. Sometimes I have to go back to the drawing board many times because my chosen solutions don't work. Other times I couldn't think of a solution and had to solicit help from others. Do whatever it takes to get on the right path and overcome obstacles. The secret is to never give up!

Another key to success is to avoid putting ourselves into compromising positions. Investing in small insurances now prevents us from paying a heavy premium later. Here is a list of safety precautions that can protect us from harm and minimize its damaging effects.

- Spend quality time with God.
- Attend church regularly.
- Pray throughout the day.
- Read your Bible daily.

- Memorize Scripture.
- Put on the armor of God (Eph. 6:10–18).
- Read materials that help you grow in Christ.
- Confess your sins daily.
- Be careful of what you watch, read, and listen to.
- Cultivate healthy, positive relationships.
- Keep junk foods out of the house.
- Purchase healthy foods.
- Prepare snacks in advance.
- Expand your food horizons to include a healthy variety.

Call to Action

1. Name at least two safety precautions that can prevent you from getting off course.
2. What is missing from your prayer time—adoration? submission? petition? intercession? confession? When will you add this practice to your prayers?
3. Identify a problem you are having. How will you apply the four steps to solving it?
4. What action is God prompting you to take?

Lord, I thank You for always giving me a way of escape when I am tempted. Help me to use the power You gave me to set up and maintain safety precautions. Give me wisdom to know which safety measures to take and discernment to recognize when I am headed down the wrong path. Bless me to choose the path of righteousness instead of the path of destruction. In Jesus' name I pray. Amen.

Strategy Four

DON'T CONFORM
TO THE WORLD

Chapter 12

DRESS DIFFERENTLY

*W*HEN I GAINED *seven pounds during the holiday season, I found myself resorting to my old way of thinking. I thought I could eat anything I wanted and easily lose the weight. All I had to do was give up a snack here or there or go without eating for half a day.*

The pounds stacked on, and I convinced myself I would lose the weight once the holidays were over. That didn't happen. One day in my desperation, I found myself searching through cabinets for the bottle of fat-burner capsules I had purchased the year before. My old thinking said, "These will take off the weight!" I took them for a week while continuing to eat high-fat foods and desserts. I acted as if my actions had no consequences. What was I thinking?

Instead of using self-discipline, eating less, making healthier choices, and exercising to burn calories, I chose to take the easy way out. The "easy" way, however, ended up causing more problems. I felt nauseous and sickly the entire week I took the fat burners, plus I gained more weight from the high-fat foods I ate. I paid a higher price by trying to take the easy way out.

I resorted to the world's way of doing things and found myself distanced from God, lethargic, with an overall feeling of malaise, and seven pounds heavier. Yielding to my flesh rather than the Spirit afforded me only a few minutes of pleasure, but months of pain.

> Now the mind of the flesh [which is sense and reason without the Holy Spirit] is death [death that comprises all the miseries arising

from sin, both here and hereafter]. But the mind of the [Holy] Spirit is life and [soul] peace [both now and forever].

—Romans 8:6 AMP

SPIRITUAL FASHION STATEMENT

In the first part of Romans 12:2, we are commanded not to be conformed to the world. According to *Vine's Complete Expository Dictionary of Old and New Testament Words,* the word "conformed" in this verse is from the Greek word *suschematizo,* which means "to fashion or shape one thing like another."[1]

This means we are not to fashion ourselves like the world or gain its acceptance by copying its fads, fashions, behaviors, and customs. Instead, God calls us to be transformed by permanently changing our thinking for the better so it is holy and pleasing to Him. I will go into detail about what it means to be transformed in a later chapter.

In Genesis, we read of the origin of humankind. God made people in His image. He created us to be like Him. Complicating matters is that when God made us, He gave us free will, which allows us to choose whether we will obey Him. However, since God is holy, we are to be holy too (Lev. 19:2). Still, we are free to choose to live in a righteous or a worldly, fleshly manner.

TO CHANGE OR NOT TO CHANGE

Upon further exploration of the word "conformed," I discovered it refers to something that is transitory, changeable, and unstable.[2] This definition accurately describes the world (the system in which we live that promotes evil and self over anything having to do with God). The world is transitory—lasting for only a time; changeable—variable and inconsistent; and unstable—changing or wavering.

It is interesting to note that God is unchanging. He is the same today as He was in the past and will forever be in the future. When we choose to be like God, we choose the better way—stability rather than instability.

Those who live according to the world are always changing. They panic and change their spending habits when the economy changes; they change their overall appearance when new fads come along, and they switch beliefs when new doctrines arise. Whatever they do lasts only for a time, and they experience various degrees of instability.

Those who live according to God and the Word are stable and steady. Despite changes in the economy, fads, and doctrines, they remain fixed and unwavering in their beliefs, values, attitudes, and actions because they are fashioned after God and not after the things in the world.

Before salvation, we live like the world because we don't know any better. First Peter 1:14 (AMP) instructs believers to "[Live] as children of obedience [to God]; do not conform yourselves to the evil desires [that governed you] in your former ignorance [when you did not know the requirements of the Gospel]." Once we are saved, we are to obey God and stop fashioning our lives after the world's way of doing things.

OUTWARD FASHIONS

Suschematizo in Romans 12:2 is not speaking of an inward transformation but of being outwardly "conformed." It is referring to the way we live, how we act, and what we do. Romans 12:2 commands us to not be outwardly fashioned after the world, but to live in a way that is different from the norm. Our language, actions, and attitudes should be different from those of the world and modeled after Christ.

Those of us fashioned after God are careful about the things we say. Our speech is wholesome, building others up and free from anger, rage, malice, slander, lies, filthy language, and coarse joking (Eph. 4:29, 5:4; Col. 3:8; 4:6). We are careful about the things we choose to look at (Ps. 101:3; 119:37; Prov. 4:25). We do not look at others with lust, and we refuse to cast our sights on anything vile or vulgar. We avoid listening to music, movies, TV shows, and conversations that are filthy, degrading, obscene, and dishonoring to God.

We are also careful of what we subject our bodies to—be it sexual immorality, idolatry, witchcraft, greed, or gluttony—because our bodies are temples of God. We honor God with our bodies (Rom. 6:13; Gal. 5:19–21; Eph. 5:3; 1 Cor. 6:19–20). Honoring God with our bodies includes *not* going to certain places and *not* hanging around certain people if doing so dishonors God.

If we are not conformed to the world, there is a noticeable difference in us that represents holiness, godliness, and moral integrity. People see we are different from the world by the way we dress (we don't wear things that tempt others sexually), the way we talk (we don't utter sinful things), and the way we act (our bodies are undefiled).

BAD COMPANY DOESN'T FIT

The Bible tells us to be careful of those we hang around because bad company corrupts good character (1 Cor. 15:33). We tend to take on (conform to) the habits, attitudes, and mannerisms of the people around us; therefore, it makes sense to stay away from those who indulge in wrong behaviors. In order to continue in righteousness, we must surround ourselves with people striving for godliness.

We get into trouble when we let others coax us into doing what goes against God's instructions and against what we know to be right. This happened to Saul when he lost the kingdom for allowing his men to pressure him into offering sacrifices rather than waiting for Samuel the priest to offer them (1 Sam. 13:1–4).

ENGAGE YOUR RIGHTEOUSNESS GAUGE

We must set strict boundaries to avoid worldly temptations. Loosening godly boundaries, even the slightest bit, makes room for conformity. When little ungodly practices are allowed to take place, before we know it, we've lost sight of what was right to begin with. "Little" compromises cause adjustments to the God-compass inside of us, resulting in our righteousness gauge being offset. Pretty soon, our estimation of righteousness is far from what truly is righteous, and we are aligned with what is worldly.

I find this to be the case in my eating. My righteousness gauge in regard to food says I must limit sugary sweets to no more than one every other day. When I compromise and eat sugary sweets two days in a row, my body alerts me that I'm getting off-kilter. If I ignore the warning and eat something sweet a third day, my body begins to have trouble determining the reason for the boundary. *Why do I have a sugar limit? I've had sweets three days in a row and I feel fine, so it must be OK to have them more often. Having them more doesn't seem to hurt. I'm OK right now, aren't I? Do I really need a limit?*

I ruin my righteousness gauge when I ignore boundaries. Eating sweets for a fourth day strengthens my flesh in a way that causes it to become unruly. It practically screams for what it wants: *"Give me more junk!"* The once-tamed monster is unleashed when I ignore boundaries. My flesh takes over, and my righteousness gauge loses the power to guide. All the while, the Holy Spirit beckons me not to give in: *Resist the temptation and go back to what God told you to do.*

During the holidays, I ignored boundaries and lost my senses. I ignored the voice of God bidding me to stop. I ended up far off course, and it took a lot of time and effort to recover the ground I lost. I am extremely grateful I was able to recover. Recall Saul, mentioned earlier in this chapter. He never did regain the kingdom; God took it from him and gave it to David.

CALIBRATE YOUR GAUGE

To remain on course and not conformed to the world, we need to keep God at the center of our decisions. It is OK for someone else to eat foods God instructs me not to eat. That person may or may not experience the ill effects I would if I disobeyed God and ate. God lets us know the boundaries we need that will keep us from falling into temptation. Things that tempt one person may not tempt another. We cannot afford to make personal decisions based on what is OK for someone else to do. Our decisions should be based upon God's will for us so we don't end up in unfortunate situations.

We don't have to give in to temptation, because God always provides a way of escape. It is, however, up to us to take that way. The sooner we resist temptation, the better. Resisting temptation at its onset means no lost ground. When we give in to temptation, we face consequences, and the severity of the consequences depends upon how far we stray from righteousness.

WEAR GOD'S DESIGNER LABEL

God wants us to be clearly identified as His children. When we try to fit in with certain people or groups who are not Christian, we conform.

We are to be set apart, which may cause some people to dislike us, but it causes God to be pleased with us. Pleasing God and not people should be our priority. We cannot afford to compromise our position with God to gain favor with people.

For example, my husband and I usually attend our company parties, where free drinks are often served. Usually, everyone around us drinks and tries to get us to drink, even though we explain that we don't. We are offered "just one drink" and told, "How about a little wine? It won't hurt." We stand our ground and hold fast to our convictions, even though everyone around us, including our supervisors, takes advantage of free drinks.

There were times when we stuck out like sore thumbs because everyone else drank. It would have been easier to give in just to fit in with the group and score points with the boss. Yet we didn't compromise our values and held fast to our boundaries. In the end, I saw how my husband and I actually were esteemed by our co-workers. We were viewed as people who were dependable and trustworthy because we held to our values.

FASHIONED AFTER GOD

We must make a commitment—at all costs—to righteousness. We may lose friends or family or suffer loss of status or financial resources, but which is worse: losing a right standing with God or a temporary standing with people?

When I began my healthy eating journey over a year ago, I gave up hanging out with my old eating buddies. When I was with them, all we did was eat and eat and eat. We didn't see anything wrong with pigging out. We thought it was fun. That was my old life. Now I'm committed to following God's eating plan for me. Being found as good, acceptable, and pleasing to God is more important to me than binges and uncontrolled eating.

We cannot serve both God and Satan, nor can we be both righteous and worldly. We won't be found pleasing to God if we dabble in sin and worldliness. We must not compromise our godly standards to fit in with the world. God commands us to not conform to the world. Instead, we are to fashion ourselves to be like Him so we can be found as holy, acceptable, and pleasing in His sight.

Call to Action

1. Would those who know you best say you are godly or worldly?
2. What do you do that might cause someone to believe you are godly?
3. What things do you do that might cause someone to believe you are worldly?
4. What things do you need to change in order not to be conformed to the world?
5. What action is God prompting you to take?

Lord, please bless me not to be conformed to the world. Bless me to be for You a light who radiates godliness in this dark world. Give me spiritual discernment to recognize when I am becoming like the world, and immediately convict me in a way that leads to prompt repentance. In Jesus' name I pray. Amen.

Chapter 13

FIND TRUE FREEDOM

YESTERDAY I SAW a new natural-health doctor. I left with a six-page list of foods I should eat and foods I should avoid, based upon my blood type. I was also given a guideline for the "best" kind of breakfast to eat for optimal energy, complete nutrition, improved digestion, weight loss ... blah, blah, blah. The list went on and on. The optimal breakfast included eating a mixture of five vegetables and five proteins so my body gets the nutrients it needs for energy and assimilation. I felt like I needed schooling just to understand the food combinations and amounts needed.

At this point in my life, this is too much work! I want to be healthy, and I know it will take hard work, but surely this isn't what Jesus had in mind when He said to care for our temples. Frankly, this blood-type plan felt more like a form of bondage than something leading to freedom. I want health, but I also want to live free!

"Take my yoke upon you. Let me teach you, because I am humble and gentle at heart, and you will find rest for your souls. For my yoke is easy to bear, and the burden I give you is light."
—Matthew 11:29–30 NLT

UTTER FOOLISHNESS

There is much nonsense out there masquerading as legitimate diets and healthful living. I'm not referring to eating plans that are reasonable and

91

balanced. I'm talking about those kooky plans that call for ridiculous and unhealthy limiting of calories, eating only one or two foods, or eating only expensive prepackaged foods—and I have I tried a bunch of them!

I have lived on grapefruit and cabbage soup for days. I have limited my diet to *only* meats and fats, *only* vegetables, *only* fat-free foods, and *only* high-protein and low-carbohydrate foods. I have tried drinking meal-replacement shakes, eating small meals every two to three hours, following specific daily meal plans, following strict diets during the week which allow free-for-all binges on the weekend, as well as other limiting and restricting plans. None of these offered lasting solutions.

In my desperation, I attempted even more irrational weight-loss efforts. I tried bingeing and purging, taking weight-loss pills (over-the-counter and mail-order), appetite suppressants, fat burners, and fat blockers. I tried costly weight-loss programs, wearing plastic sweat suits, wearing fat-burning shorts, listening to subliminal-message tapes, and even hypnosis. As I write this, I'm thoroughly embarrassed by the extreme lengths I went through to lose weight. It's silly to think I did all of these things to take weight off the "easy" way, rather than simply changing my eating and my exercise habits.

Truly, none of these ways were easy. I paid a high price for every single one of them, monetarily and physically. I wasted a lot of money buying foods I didn't eat, paying for programs I didn't like, and purchasing pills that made me sick. I threw my hormones out of whack, eating everything soy in an effort not to eat meat and animal products. I messed up my blood-sugar levels eating a high-carbohydrate diet. I got dehydrated wearing a dumb plastic suit, trying to melt away fat. I disrupted my sleep by listening to weird noises and excessive talking on subliminal tapes. I felt utterly stupid repeating silly phrases during my hypnosis sessions. I dealt with headaches and episodes of nausea, had the jitters, and experienced times of weakness from the many things I tried.

When I take a step back and look at scriptural truths, I realize what I did was absolutely foolish. In Matthew 11:29–30, Jesus says, "Take My yoke upon you and learn from Me, for My yoke is easy and My burden is light." I wanted what was easy and I wanted to be lighter, but I went about it the wrong way. I looked to a lost world for answers and found myself sick, bound, and burdened from following the wrong plans. Had

I looked to the all-knowing and all-powerful Jesus Christ, I would have found the ease, relief, and refreshment I was looking for. Being yoked with Jesus is the only way to get these results.

GET YOKED

A yoke is a wooden beam fastened over the necks of two animals. The yoke allows them to plow or pull a load more easily and in sync with each other. In Matthew 11:29, Jesus tells us to take His yoke upon ourselves. When we do, we have the benefit of His wisdom, strength, and power helping us every step of the way. Putting on His yoke is better than anything else we can possibly do, because His yoke brings relief, refreshment, and recreation when we wear it (Matt. 11:29 AMP). We get yoked with God when we obey His Word and follow the leading of the Holy Spirit. Doing so gives us rest from the difficulties we are bound to face living in this world.

I carried a huge burden trying to lose weight on my own while following the wisdom of the world. I worked extremely hard trying not to eat certain foods and forcing myself to eat others. I also experienced negative health effects from many of the things I tried. But when I became yoked with Christ, everything became easier—not easy but easier. I no longer carried the weight of following diet plans, nor did I feel deprived and tormented. Following the Holy Spirit's leading about what to eat, I began to enjoy food. Now I don't feel stress about what to eat, and I feel lightness and joy from the relief I found by being yoked with Christ and letting Him lead.

In the Amplified Bible's rendition of Matthew 11:29–30, Jesus says, "Take My yoke upon you and learn of Me, for I am gentle (meek) and humble (lowly) in heart, and you will find rest (relief and ease and refreshment and recreation and blessed quiet) for your souls. For My yoke is wholesome (useful, good—not harsh, hard, sharp, or pressing, but comfortable, gracious, and pleasant), and My burden is light and easy to be borne." Jesus tells us to learn of Him how to be yoked with Him. Doing so leads to rest—relief, ease, refreshment, recreation, and blessed quiet—for our souls. We can learn more about Him by studying the Bible. In it we find a written account of His life, the stories He told, and the things He said and did. Following His example, along with obeying the Bible, yokes us with Him and causes His presence to go with us, giving us rest (Exod. 33:14).

WHAT IS BONDAGE?

Before studying the word *bondage*, I knew it meant a state of being restrained or held captive. But when I looked further, I was surprised to find the depth and variety of its meaning. From the following definitions, I saw clearly the bondage I was under trying to lose weight the world's way.

1. The state of being under the control of a force or influence or abstract power[1]
    (I sought the world to help me with my eating and weight issues.)
2. The state of being under the control of another person[2]
    (I followed the advice of people, along with their programs and their products.)
3. The state of being a slave[3]
    (I did what I was told, even when it wasn't beneficial or pleasing to me.)
4. A state of being greatly constrained by circumstances or obligations[4]
    (Great restrictions were placed on what and when I could and could not eat.)
5. Slavery or involuntary servitude; serfdom[5]
    (I did not enjoy following the strict guidelines that took away my freedom of choice.)
6. The state of being bound by or subjected to some external power or control[6]
    (My daily life was limited and constricted by the strict guidelines of whatever program or plans I followed.)
7. The state of being under obligation, restraint, or captivity[7]
    (Having paid for programs and products, I felt obligated to follow their advice and lived as a prisoner in my own body.)

I combined these definitions into one of my own: *Bondage is the state of being involuntarily constrained under obligation, captivity, or control by a force or external power, as if a slave.*

I found myself in bondage following the world's advice, even after I'd read about the ease that comes from being yoked with Christ. Following the world's ways, I was held captive by doctors, programs, meal plans, pills, and products. I wasn't free to make my own decisions about what I ate, but followed strict guidelines and stayed within boundaries that deprived me of joy. I felt confined adhering to these limits. I found *nothing* liberating about any of the things I tried.

WHAT IS FREEDOM?

Freedom is the opposite of bondage. I looked up "freedom" in various sources and was surprised by the depth and variety of meaning of this word also. I began to see the freedom that comes with following Jesus Christ. I can now see that what I *thought* was freedom (the world's way of doing things) is actually bondage, and what I thought was bondage (God's way of doing things) is actually freedom.

1. The power or right to act, speak, or think as one wants without hindrance or restraint[8]
   (I am free to eat whatever I choose.)
2. Absence of subjection to foreign domination or despotic government[9]
   (God isn't a controller and doesn't force me to eat a certain way. He allows me to exercise free will to make my own decisions.)
3. The quality or state of being free: as
   - the absence of necessity, coercion, or constraint in choice or action
     (I don't have to follow restricted plans.)
   - liberation from slavery or restraint or from the power of another : independence
     (I am not under God's control, but am free to do as I please.)
   - unrestricted use <gave him the freedom of their home>[10]
     (There are no set rules for what and when I can or cannot eat.)

4. A political right; franchise, privilege[11]
   (God gives me the right and privilege to express my personal choices.)
5. The state of being free or at liberty rather than in confinement or under physical restraint[12]
   (I am free from the bondage and captivity of plans, procedures, and products.)
6. Exemption from external control, interference, regulation, etc.[13]
   (I am released to make my own food choices without any interference.)

I attempted to come up with a single definition for freedom, but I wasn't able to do so. Nothing I tried could adequately convey the word's truest meaning. Freedom means to be *free*—nothing hindering and nothing blocking. The freedom God gives is unimaginable. It is something so spacious, open, and vast that we can't wrap our minds around it. We can experience a portion of true freedom by being yoked with Christ. In Him we find rest—relief, ease, refreshment, recreation, and blessed quiet—for our souls!

FREEDOM WITHIN BOUNDARIES

God's yoke leads to freedom; the world's yoke leads to bondage. God lets us know His will and what is best for us, yet He allows us the freedom to choose our own courses of action. The world tells us what it thinks is best for us and restricts us to plans that hold us captive. Yoking ourselves to God takes away the guesswork and time it takes to discover what is best and most beneficial. Yoking ourselves with the world adds much guesswork and wasted time because the world is incapable of knowing what is best.

In God, we have freedom within boundaries. This may seem like a contradiction, but it isn't. God's boundaries are what allow us freedom and at the same time keep us safe. For example, when your child remains in a fenced yard, he is kept safe and is free to play within that boundary. The fence keeps danger out and keeps the child safe within. If the fence is removed, the child becomes unsure of how far he can go and when he's out of safety's reach. Also, without a fence, outsiders don't know the boundary lines of your yard. This makes it easier for someone to harm your child or for robbers to get in and steal.

God set the boundary lines of sin. As long as we remain within those lines, we are free to do whatever we will. When we cross the line into sin, we are no longer in the safety zone, and nothing blocks danger or the enemy from easily bringing us harm.

When we stay within the boundaries God sets for us, we are protected and have freedom. We discover what is best by following His leading. I cannot explain how, but when I consult God about what I should or shouldn't eat and follow His leading, I feel better, have more energy, and am healthier. I get all of this without feeling bondage. Instead I feel freedom, relief, ease, and refreshment!

FOOD IS GOD'S GIFT

God wants us to enjoy our lives and find pleasure in the foods we eat. In His Word, we find scriptures that show just how much He wants us to delight in His provision of food.

- God gave us all kinds of seed-bearing plants for food (Gen. 1:29).
- God allowed the Israelites to gather all the manna they could eat (Exod. 16:4–5, 13–18).
- Hard workers have plenty of food (Prov. 12:11).
- Those who are not lazy are satisfied with food (Prov. 20:13).
- Stores of choice food and oil are in wise people's houses (Prov. 21:20 NIV).
- Enjoying food is a gift of God (Eccl. 3:12–13; 5:18–19).
- Jesus fed the multitudes until they were full, and He sent the leftovers home with the disciples (Luke 9:12–17).
- God removed restrictions from forbidden foods (Acts 10:9–15).
- No food is considered forbidden or unholy to eat (Rom. 14:14).
- God provides everything for our enjoyment (1 Tim. 6:17).

These are just some of the verses about food in the Bible. Food plays an important role in the Bible. Throughout, we find references to the special gift it is. In Genesis, God gave us plants for food. In Exodus, He gave the Israelites food from heaven. In Psalms, He talks about preparing a table for us in the presence of our enemies. In Isaiah, God invites us to enjoy nourishment for free! In the Lord's Prayer, Jesus taught us to ask for our daily bread. He served His disciples the Last Supper. He even referred to Himself as the bread of life (John 6:35).

Even though God gives us freedom to enjoy food, we are to remain within boundaries. We are to avoid eating as gluttons, without self-control, which is sin and removes us from the safety zone. We are free to eat whatever we wish as long as we refrain from this.

FOOD BOUNDARIES AND FREEDOM

Even in moderation, some foods taste good but are not good for us, because they negatively affect our health by giving us gas, bloating, pain, and so forth. Those foods should be avoided. God requires us to care for our temples, and eating foods that make us feel bad (unwell) is showing disregard for our bodies. Not only that, feeling bad is a sign we've crossed the line of safety. Although we can eat anything, not everything is beneficial for us to eat (1 Cor. 6:12). The bottom line is we will experience freedom, relief, and ease if we eat in a way that brings health to our bodies.

We are free to choose how we live—following the world or following God. The world tells us prescribed formulas leading to dead ends, difficulty, and bondage. God tells us what can harm us and what keeps us safe. Then He allows us the freedom to choose the path we will take.

Call to Action

1. Evaluate your life. In what ways do you feel bound? In what ways do you feel free?
2. What keeps you in bondage?
3. What are you willing to change to live a life of freedom?
4. What action is God prompting you to take?

Lord, please forgive me for looking to the world for answers instead of looking to You. Thank You for making it possible for me to live free. Help me not to take my freedom for granted, but to use it in a way that pleases You. Deliver me from the lure of this sinful world. Teach me to yoke myself with You so I can secure rest for my soul. In Jesus' name I pray. Amen.

Strategy Five

BE TRANSFORMED

Chapter 14

FROM CATERPILLAR TO BUTTERFLY

GOD IS DEFINITELY changing me. Ever since I started living Romans 12:1–2, my eating patterns have dramatically altered. I've denied my flesh by resisting the urge to yield to its desires, and I've arduously strived to do God's will. Evidence of this change took place quite recently.

Before preparing for bed one night, I ate a portion of a cookie. A short while later, I wanted something more. I wasn't hungry, and the amount I'd eaten was enough. It had satisfied my taste buds and kept my sugar intake at a healthy limit. I was experiencing food cravings, and "flesh" was the culprit. I decided against eating the rest of the cookie and left the kitchen feeling good that I was able to stop at a piece of one cookie instead of ravaging through them all.

It seems that since I've consistently resisted the temptation to give in to junk food urges, they are losing the power to control me and are easier to overcome than they once were. I'm realizing, even in relation to food, whatever muscle we exercise is the one that gets stronger. I exercised resistance and self-control for six months, which made it easier for me to walk away from the cookies this time. When I started this journey, the junk-food muscle was strongest, and I would not have made a good choice in this situation.

Even though I resisted the cookies, my flesh didn't give up easily. I found myself back in the kitchen looking through the fridge for something else to eat. My flesh was trying its best to have its way by building up a strong desire for something sweet. I thought about giving in and drinking a fruit-juice-sweetened sparkling water, reasoning that it wasn't bad for me. My spirit quickly rose up and thundered "No!" reminding me it was still a form of sugar I didn't need before bedtime. Again, my flesh lost, but it still didn't give up.

Back in the kitchen a third time. Once again, I went to the refrigerator, since nothing sweet was in any of the cabinets. I spotted the strawberry kefir (similar to drinkable yogurt). I felt my spirit saying no for the same reason it said no to the sparkling water. I didn't need the sugar and I was not hungry. This time, instead of keeping myself near the temptation, I shut the refrigerator, drank some water, and went upstairs to prepare for bed.

"Watch and pray so that you will not fall into temptation. The spirit is willing, but the flesh is weak."

—Mark 14:38 NIV

A NEW ME

I felt proud of myself for not yielding to temptation. Not proud in an arrogant way, but proud of the accomplishment. There was a time when I gave in to every whim of my flesh. My spirit muscles were extremely weak because I hardly exercised them when it came to food. My flesh, however, had great strength and bulging muscles because I used them all the time! I thank God for teaching me to listen to His directions and giving me healthy boundaries to keep me safe and free from harm. Through the Holy Spirit's guidance, I am becoming a new person. Not just on the outside, but on the inside as well.

BEING TRANSFORMED

I am going through a metamorphosis much like the transformation a caterpillar goes through inside a chrysalis (or pupa), as it changes into a butterfly. Like a caterpillar inside a chrysalis, my insides are changing. I think differently than I used to about food. My spirit wants to eat healthy. My spirit enjoys how it feels when it makes good food choices, and it prefers to eat in a way that makes it feel good.

Making better choices comes more naturally now. Without even thinking, at the grocery store I gravitate toward purchasing fresh fruits and vegetables, dried beans and grains, and fresh meats. I rarely buy heavily processed foods. I prepare healthier meals at home by using fresh or minimally processed foods, and I incorporate fresh vegetables wherever possible. I also try to make half of whatever I put on my plate vegetables and/or fruits. When I eat out, I make a point to get plenty of vegetables. Most of the time I stay away from breads, pastas, cheeses, sauces, and desserts! Sometimes I want something unhealthy, like chips, French fries, fried chicken, or desserts, but these things are no longer the norm, and I limit the amount I eat.

Romans 12:2 tells us to be transformed in our minds. "Transformed" in the Greek comes from the word *metamorphoō*,[1] which means "to change into another form, to transform, to transfigure." It refers to an internal change, unlike "conformed," which refers to an external change. I know I'm being transformed because my thoughts about and feelings toward food have radically changed.

When a caterpillar goes through metamorphosis, it undergoes a complete change inside the chrysalis. Inside the chrysalis, its tissue structures are broken down chemically and new adult structures are formed. The completed process results in the caterpillar's transformation into a butterfly.

God is breaking down the structures of my soul (my mind, will, and emotions) and forming them into something new. I've gone from being an eating machine who once was controlled by food to a person who submits to the authority of the Holy Spirit and desires to eat appropriately.

According to the *Riverside Webster's II Dictionary*, "transform" means (1) to alter markedly the appearance or form of, and (2) to change the nature, function, or condition of : convert.[2]

I found the second definition fascinating because it describes what is happening to me. I am changing in nature, function, and condition. I'm being converted. To help our understanding of the significance of what is taking place, here are the definitions of nature, function, condition, and convert.

Nature: 1. state of existence; 2. intrinsic characteristics and qualities; 3. one's basic character or disposition : temperament

Function: the special purpose for which something exists

Condition: 1. mode or state of being; 2. a state of health or fitness; 3. existing circumstances

Convert: 1. to change into another form, substance, state or product: transform; 2. to adapt to a new or different use or purpose

In regard to food, I am undergoing a deep internal change in which my fundamental nature is being transformed by the power of God. My disposition and temperament have changed to where I no longer get an adrenaline rush simply from anticipating eating, nor do inner voices nag at me to eat excessively, and I don't feel an anxious tug to gorge myself. I no longer have an impelling desire to stop at sundry places to feed an insatiable sweet tooth. I used to get aroused at the mere *thought* of food. Every now and then, a new food or restaurant may stimulate some excitement, but I have self-control. Food does not have the final say-so in my life anymore.

In function, I no longer live to pleasure myself with food. I used to live to eat, but I now eat to live. At one time, like a caterpillar, all I wanted to do was eat and eat and eat. I didn't necessarily eat for the taste, but for the feeling of fullness. Food was a diversion from the issues in my life. I used to turn to food to tranquilize and soothe me when I had a problem. Now I deal with problems and confront issues. Now I eat to benefit my body. Yes, I sometimes eat unhealthy foods for pleasure, but not in excess the way I used to. My priority now is to make healthy choices.

I have changed in condition as well. I used to feel sluggish and sick practically all the time. I had pain in my knees and shortness of breath whenever I did anything physical. Now I feel good and possess greater energy. I look forward to physical activity. I am able to move about more quickly and freely without pain and heaviness. My health and fitness levels have dramatically improved. My blood pressure, cholesterol, and weight have all dropped significantly!

I am being transformed from existing as a food-devouring, slow-moving, somber, caterpillar-like person to a spirited, joy-filled, nimble, butterfly-like creature!

METAMORPHOSIS

A metamorphosis is

1. a complete change of form, structure, or appearance;[3] and
2. a change in form from one stage to the next in the life of an organism, as from pupa to butterfly.[4]

Metamorphosis will not happen if you are sitting around doing nothing or are waiting for change to miraculously happen. When I only prayed for change and hoped to lose weight, nothing happened … except gradual weight gain. I had to get off my rear end and start moving my body; I had to eat less and make healthier choices; I had to seek God's Word for power, guidance, and encouragement; I had to be attentive and yield to the Holy Spirit's leading.

If you want to lose excess weight (that is, pounds, addictions, bad relationships, and so on), you have to *do* something! Even a caterpillar has to continuously eat and then form itself into a chrysalis before it can change into a butterfly!

Spiritual transformation comes only through reading, understanding, practicing, and obeying God's Word. When we feed on His Word, it gets into us and becomes part of us. By the power of God, we undergo a complete change that is expressed in our character and conduct. We become more and more like Him, and our old self dies.

Along with internal changes, metamorphosis also transfigures the outer body. This is because the change that occurs on the inside requires a new external structure to carry out the function (purpose) for which we newly exist. I have a smaller physique that can handle more physical activity. As a result, I can do more to help build the kingdom of God. This same thing happens during the metamorphosis of a butterfly. Once a caterpillar is transformed into a butterfly—changed in nature, function, and condition—it stops being a multilegged, ground-wriggling, wormy-looking thing that only eats and grows. It becomes a beautiful winged adult that migrates, mates, reproduces, and colonizes new habitats.

But metamorphoses of butterflies and people also are very different. The adult butterfly is the final stage of caterpillar metamorphosis. Once this stage is complete, the adult butterfly lives only a short while. For those of us who surrender our lives to Christ, the transformation process continues throughout our lifetime. While we are on earth, we are ever transformed into God's likeness with ever-increasing glory (2 Cor. 3:18 NIV). Metamorphosis will not end until we get to heaven and receive a glorified body that will last throughout eternity (1 Cor. 15:42–44, 49; Phil. 3:20–21).

INTERNAL CHANGES

The changes that take place inside the chrysalis are quite interesting. According to Gordon Ramel,[5] the caterpillar's old body dies. It is attacked by the same juices the caterpillar used in its earlier life to digest its food. In essence, the caterpillar digests itself from the inside out, but not all of the tissue is destroyed. Some of the old tissue passes on to its new self. The caterpillar contains special cells that help it to build a new body out of the soup left from its old body.

This change can be likened to what happens when plastic is recycled. Once an object begins the recycling process, it is melted down and formed into an entirely new shape. In the end, it is made into something useful and serves an entirely new purpose.

When we accept Jesus Christ as our personal Savior, we begin the process of transformation. Our old sinful man is destroyed—but not all of it. Our soul (mind, will, and emotions) does not die. Instead, it is transformed from being sinful in nature, function, and condition into something new in Christ (Rom. 6:6–8; 2 Cor. 5:17; Eph. 2:1, 4–5). During this process, we also undergo sanctification—God's cleansing process—which makes us like Jesus (1 Cor. 1:2; Heb. 10:10).

As we are changed, we gain the mind of Christ (1 Cor. 2:16), desire to do God's will (Ps. 40:8), and live more honorably in everything we do (Heb. 13:18). This remarkable change enables us to fulfill our greatest purpose—to serve God and not ourselves.

PRAY TO DIE

In order to honor God and experience metamorphosis, we must die to our old self (our old sinful nature). When we die to self, we end up with a renewed mind, possessing a fresh mental and spiritual attitude

(Eph. 4:22–24 AMP). Ironically, if we die to ourselves—strip ourselves of our old ways—we live again in Christ!

If you want to experience this new life in Christ, begin by praying the following prayer:

> Dear Lord, I make a mess of my life whenever I choose to do things my way instead of Yours. Please forgive me for not doing things Your way and for not obeying You. I'm sorry I haven't let You be Lord of my life. Forgive me. I realize my life is not my own. Because You created me and sent Your Son, Jesus, to die for my sins, I no longer want to live for myself but for You. I invite Jesus to come into my heart and be Lord of my life. I die to myself so I can be set free from the power of sin. I submit my will to Yours. I am now Your servant, because You created me for Your good pleasure. In the name of Jesus I pray. Amen.

After you've died to yourself and started living for Christ, you *will* see the power of God manifested in your life. Like me, one day you will realize you are no longer like a caterpillar but are being made into something new! If you seek and obey God, and let him have His way in your life, guaranteed remarkable changes are in store for you!

Call to Action

1. What do you need to die to?
2. Where will you be in one, five, or twenty years if you continue doing things your own way?
3. Pray and ask God what you should do to better your life. What did He tell you? (Be patient. It may take some time for you to hear His answer.)
4. What action is God prompting you to take?

Lord God, please remove the blinders from my eyes. Help me see what is causing me to be separated from You. Have mercy on me. Please change my heart so I am eager to die to myself and live for You. Make me into something new that will bring much glory and honor to You. In the name of Jesus I pray. Amen.

Chapter 15

LIVIN' AND WALKIN'

E *VEN THOUGH I'VE changed a lot and have walked this Romans
12:1–2 road for months, I sometimes find myself in a place I feel I
shouldn't be. It's embarrassing to have to admit I still struggle with food. I
know in my head I shouldn't feel ashamed, because God is still working on
me, and I'm never going to be sin free or perfect until I reach heaven. Still,
I'm deeply saddened I continue to give in to temptation.*

*Why do I still give in to my flesh when doing so makes me feel so miser-
able? Why do I allow myself to reap negative consequences for short stints
of pleasure? Is it because I'm still in the process of transformation? I wish I
could use that as an excuse. Regrettably, I think a major part of my problem
is I live in the Spirit, but I don't always walk in the Spirit.*

> If we live by the [Holy] Spirit, let us also walk by the Spirit. [If by
> the Holy Spirit we have our life in God, let us go forward walking in
> line, our conduct controlled by the Spirit.]
> —Galatians 5:25 AMP

SPIRITUAL CONNECTIONS

As I continue on this Romans 12:1–2 journey, I discover greater truths
about the Word and more things about myself. My latest discovery
revealed another reason I continue to give in to food: I don't always
walk in the Spirit.

I didn't realize there was a difference between living and walking in the Spirit until I studied Galatians 5:16–17. I compared and contrasted five translations and then studied the Greek of these verses. Even though some versions of these verses appear to use "live" and "walk" interchangeably, living and walking in the Spirit are very different things. Here are the two versions I studied, which helped me see the difference between living and walking in the Spirit, and why I continue to have food and flesh battles.

> This I say then, Walk in the Spirit, and ye shall not fulfill the lust of the flesh. For the flesh lusteth against the Spirit, and the Spirit against the flesh: and these are contrary the one to the other: so that ye cannot do the things that ye would.
>
> —Galatians 5:16–17 KJV

> So I say, live by the Spirit, and you will not gratify the desires of the sinful nature. For the sinful nature desires what is contrary to the Spirit, and the Spirit what is contrary to the sinful nature. They are in conflict with each other, so that you do not do what you want.
>
> —Galatians 5:16–17 NIV

Rather than give the Greek definitions of all the words in these verses, I have paraphrased what I learned.

First, verse 16: *Everywhere you go, and at all times, let your behavior show that your life is joined firmly to the current of God that blows through you by the Holy Spirit, and devoutly live a life of worship to God, so you completely terminate your human longings, affections, and corrupt fleshly tendencies. Doing so, you will come to the place where you fully carry out God's will because you are responsive to, controlled, and guided by the breath of the Holy Spirit.*

My overall behavior shows my devotion to God and that the Holy Spirit is flowing through me, but there's a problem. Remnants of my old nature still remain. The remaining longings, affections, and tendencies are in the process of becoming completely responsive to and controlled by the Holy Spirit. The Spirit is working to convert my old fleshly tendencies to new godly ones. This change can be likened to what happened when television programming changed from analog to digital.

Converter Boxes

On June 12, 2009, all full-power TV stations ended their regular programming on analog signals and switched exclusively to digital broadcasting of television programming.[1] Some low-power stations were permitted to continue analog broadcasts because they broadcasted at very low power to small community areas.[2] By September 1, 2015, however, all analog television transmitters must shut down.[3]

This switch to digital broadcasting affected everyone with analog reception on their television sets, because analog TVs are unable to receive over-the-air digital broadcasts without a converter box or a subscription to cable or satellite service. Nowadays, if you want to watch TV, you must have cable, satellite, or a TV with a built-in digital tuner. Without those, a converter box is very important because it allows you to receive digital signals, which allow you to watch digital television broadcasts. Without a converter box on an analog TV, you'll either get a blank screen or fuzzy static.

A converter box helps to explain what happens to us as we become completely responsive to and controlled by the Holy Spirit.

Before I began this Romans 12:1–2 journey, as far as food was concerned, my flesh sent signals that were self-serving, unrighteous, and distorted. It craved food in ways that were extremely harmful to my body. It wanted to eat anything and everything, no matter how bad it made me feel or how unhealthy it was.

As I began my journey, my "full-power stations," like eating too much and making unhealthy food choices, were converted to eating smaller portions and eating more fruits and vegetables. I refer to these as "full-power stations" because these desires dominated and caused pervasive harm to my body.

My "low-powered stations," like craving fatty and sweet foods, are still in the process of being converted and will one day be completely shut down.

In spiritual terms, Jesus Christ is my converter box. He makes it possible for me to receive the Holy Spirit. The Holy Spirit works to switch my flesh signals to Christ's righteousness, making me acceptable to God. When my initial conversion took place (when I first accepted

Jesus Christ as my Lord and Savior), major parts of my old sin nature were immediately converted, and I became righteous *positionally*. Every time I resist temptation, don't give in to fleshly desires, and submit to Christ's authority, I become righteous *experientially*.

Broadcast Signals

Now let's take a look at my paraphrase of Galatians 5:17: *All Christians have flesh and the [Holy] Spirit as part of their bodies. Your flesh, the outer covering of your body and your sinful human nature, which doesn't include your soul or your spirit, has feelings, passions, and desires. These desires include things like sexual immorality, jealously, anger, and drunkenness, which are contrary to God. The Holy Spirit, the current of God flowing through you, desires for God's will to be done in your life. The two, the flesh and the Spirit, are absolutely not compatible! They are offensive to each other, and both are set on getting their way. The flesh is set against the Spirit, and the Spirit opposes the flesh. Even though they are both part of you, there is great hostility between them. This consistent incompatibility between the two makes it extremely difficult for you to do the good and godly things you desire to do with your new nature.*

Things that bring our flesh pleasure don't arouse our spirits at all. The flesh (the outer covering of our bodies and our sinful natures) has separate senses and feelings that do not affect our spirits. Sensitive nerve endings in our flesh respond to things like touch and stimulation. Our flesh desires stimulation, and when desire is fulfilled, physical sensations arise that allow us to experience pleasure in a way our spirits cannot. The Holy Spirit in us is not aroused by touch, stimulation, or our senses. The Spirit responds only to the will of God.

In a spiritual sense, our flesh's sole purpose is self-gratification. It pursues whatever allows it to experience pleasure. The flesh is also greedy and thoughtless. It seeks gratification from harmful and sinful things like drugs, overeating, fornication, and sexual perversions. It doesn't stop to think about the consequences or problems these things can cause. Some of us get into trouble because our flesh seeks unrestrained pleasure from food, while the Spirit in us desires us to have self-control.

WATCH OUT FOR YOUR TONGUE

The tongue is made of flesh. Therefore, it has its own set of feelings, passions, and desires. Inside our mouths are taste buds, which God designed to give us pleasure from the foods we eat. They detect whether what we eat is bitter, salty, sour, or sweet. Our tongues also have nerve endings that allow us to enjoy the way certain foods feel in our mouths. Our spirits do not respond to the taste or feel of food.

If you eat something tasty, like a hot fudge brownie sundae with nuts and whipped cream, your [tongue] flesh immediately sends loud and clear messages to your brain about how good that sundae tastes and feels inside your mouth. Your brain sends an immediate response back to your flesh. That response is received by your sensitive human nature. If it likes what it tastes and feels, it will beckon for more.

The Spirit doesn't send these types of sensory messages. Instead, He sends spiritual messages based on truth and what's best for us. He guides us toward what will lead to life (both now and in eternity) and not death. The Spirit doesn't care about appeasing the flesh, but seeks to transform our souls and spirits.

If the Spirit tells us not to eat that sundae, but we eat it anyway because our flesh isn't in tune with the Spirit, we strengthen the flesh and awaken a desire for more. Eating one sundae isn't a sin. We cross the threshold into sin, however, when we overeat, lack self-control, or eat to the point where we feel ill.

The "low-power stations" of my flesh that crave fatty and sweet foods have the potential of going against the current of the Spirit. An occasional sweet or fattening food isn't a problem. The problem comes when I keep giving in to my flesh when it desires more and more. The Spirit tells me to limit unhealthy things to keep my cholesterol and blood-sugar levels in check so my temple is suitable for a holy God. My flesh, however, doesn't care about health or righteousness. All it cares about is self-gratification. Hence, the conflict!

The Spirit communicates God's truths to me. He gently warns me of foods I shouldn't eat because He knows what's beneficial for me. He whispers when I've had enough of something before I commit the sin of overeating and attempts to lead me down a different path. He quietly shows me how to resist my flesh every step of the way. And He will do the same for you!

Unlike the flesh, which is thoughtless and boisterous, the Spirit is wise and soft-spoken. You must carefully listen for what He is saying, or you'll miss it. It's when I let the shouting of my flesh override the whispering of the Spirit that I give in to the flesh.

STAY IN FORMATION

For many of us, our habitual conduct is in line with the Holy Spirit, but some of the steps of our walk aren't always in line with the Spirit's promptings. Sometimes we walk to fleshly calls. When we do, conviction lets us know we're out of formation and out of sync with the Spirit; then we can quickly get ourselves back in line.

Walking in the Spirit means we are taking forward steps that align with the Holy Spirit, much like a company of soldiers marching in straight lines. They stay in perfect step with their leader, and they make any corrections necessary to stay that way. Likewise, we should follow the calls of our commander, the Holy Spirit. We should adhere to His direction and conform to His commands.

FORGE AHEAD

It's interesting to note the definition of *walk*. Even though the definition refers to physical walking, there is a spiritual connation. To walk is

1. to move along or travel on foot at a moderate rate; advance in such a manner that at least one foot is always on the ground;
2. to pass through, on, or over on foot, especially habitually; and
3. to follow a certain course or way of life.[4]

We can see "walking" means to move along, advance, or pass through. It also means to follow a certain course. As we walk in the Spirit, we are able to move along in life without getting caught up in sin and its consequences. We are also able to pass through tempting situations without giving in. If we follow the particular course the Spirit has laid out for us, we will advance. We are not to follow our own course, the dictates of the flesh, or the way we think we should go. If we do, we'll cease to make progress because we'll be sidetracked by sin.

SPIRITUAL TRAILS

As we walk in the Spirit, some of our paths are easier than others to navigate. Sometimes we travel uphill and other times in valleys. Sometimes we trudge through murky waters or trek through rocky places. Sometimes we saunter through flowery fields or stroll through lush green pastures. When the terrain changes, we must not fall out of rank. We must continue to obey the voice of the all-knowing commander, the Holy Spirit. He knows the best way to navigate any trail.

Sometimes on this journey with food, I am able to traipse along without being hyperfocused on potential danger, because I'm in a place that poses no obstacles or threats. For example, I don't eat the way I used to. Now when I'm at a restaurant, I typically order a hearty portion of vegetables and skip large amounts of pasta and bread. But sometimes eating out can be like trudging through rough terrain. When a table of tantalizing desserts is in front of me, I must carefully watch my step so I don't fall into a sinkhole of a sugar binge.

It doesn't matter how we travel the course—stride, stroll, trudge, trek, hike, amble, or toddle—we must advance! Regardless of the terrain—flat, mountainous, rocky, or swampy—we must listen to the voice of the Holy Spirit so we can navigate it without falling into sin.

WALKING BENEFITS

Walking is good for us, not only spiritually but also physically. I stated in an earlier chapter the importance of physical activity. God created us to be physically active, and walking is one of the best forms of exercise. It is a natural part of our daily routine, such as walking to the restroom or to the kitchen for something to eat. It doesn't wear us out like other aerobic exercise. It's easy on the joints and easier to sustain for longer periods of time than most other forms of exercise. It builds bone density and strengthens the heart. Plus it can be done at practically any age!

According to the Mayo Clinic,[5] walking is a low-impact exercise with numerous health benefits. It trims the waistline, melts abdominal fat, and improves our health. Brisk walking can reduce the risk of heart attack by the same amount as more vigorous exercise, such as jogging.

The Mayo Clinic says walking can help you

- lower your low-density lipoprotein (LDL) cholesterol (the "bad" cholesterol);
- raise your high-density lipoprotein (HDL) cholesterol (the "good" cholesterol);
- lower your blood pressure;
- manage your weight;
- improve your mood; and
- stay strong and fit.

According to the eMedTV website,[6] brisk walking is considered a moderate-level physical activity. If you engage in thirty minutes of brisk walking on most days of the week, you will see health benefits. You can even divide the thirty minutes into shorter periods of at least ten minutes each.

Based on research, eMedTV claims walking on a regular basis has additional health benefits:

- It reduces your risk of dying from heart disease or stroke.
- It lowers your risk of heart disease, stroke, high blood pressure, colon cancer, and diabetes.
- It may help protect against certain types of cancer, such as breast cancer.
- It increases the number of calories your body uses, which helps to control your weight.
- It helps control joint swelling and pain from arthritis.

The site also claims walking can make you feel better, because it

- helps keep your bones, muscles, and joints healthy;
- reduces anxiety and depression, boosting your mood;
- helps you handle stress;
- helps you feel more energetic;

- helps you sleep better;
- improves your self-esteem; and
- gives you an opportunity to socialize actively with friends and family.

According to the City of Cambridge Community Development Department,[7] walking is good for your heart. They noted a recent Harvard study that shows walking at a moderate pace (three miles per hour) for up to three hours a week—or thirty minutes a day—can cut the risk of heart disease in women by as much as 40 percent. This is the same benefit gained from aerobics, jogging, or other vigorous exercise.

Cambridge notes a few more benefits of walking:

- It improves circulation.
- It helps breathing.
- It helps prevent osteoporosis.
- It helps prevent and control diabetes.

Walking keeps you fit and helps you lose weight and keep it off. Obesity has become an epidemic among Americans, just like carnality is a problem among Christians. Walking can cure both of these problems: physical walking can cure obesity and walking in the Spirit can cure carnality.

ENCOURAGE YOURSELF

Should you get off step, and you will, don't stay long. Quickly shake it off and get back in line. Remember, God's people are not perfect. As long as we are making steady progress, God knows our hearts are in the right place. God will still love us and won't think badly of us. Do you recall how God referred to David as a man after His own heart even though David had committed adultery with Bathsheba *and* killed her husband?

There are many people in the Bible who didn't obey God, got weak, or fell into sin. Adam and Eve disobeyed God when they ate from the tree of the knowledge of good and evil (Genesis 3), Elijah lost his courage and hid from Jezebel (1 Kings 19), and Peter denied Jesus three times (Luke 22). God forgave and loved them anyway!

Even when we commit grave sins, God has loving thoughts toward us and restores us by His love. Somewhere down the line, I'll probably lose sight of His grace and beat up on myself again when I sin or miss the mark, but in this moment I accept that I'm forgiven, loved, and highly esteemed by my Father. Besides, I am walking. I am making progress. I *am* moving ahead. I'm not staying in the same place, which is all God asks of us.

Remember to encourage yourself in the Lord like David did in 1 Samuel 30. He sought the Lord when he felt weak and defeated, and he was able to find strength and new direction. Remind yourself of scriptural truths to help you stay encouraged. And do it often so you never forget God loves you and thinks highly of you.

When I was going through a time of defeat and self-doubt, I wrote the following truths, every word of which came straight from a Bible passage. After all, only God's truth can give us the strength we need to overcome and be victors. For a time, I read this paragraph every day. Feel free to use it if you need encouragement and incentive to faithfully walk in the Spirit.

God's Word tells me I am above only and not beneath, the head and not the tail, a lender and not a borrower, chosen, strong, equipped, sufficient, awesomely and wonderfully and reverently made, anointed, appointed, highly favored, self-sufficient in Christ's sufficiency, bold, ready for anything, equal to anything, an heir, sanctified, holy, successful, rich, prosperous, good, protected, covered, free, kept, victorious, loved, honored, justified, pure, blessed, very good, counted, saved, called, a light, virtuous, healed, armed, redeemed, established, approved of, qualified, foreordained, confident, righteous, fit, whole, valued, gifted, and accepted!

KEEP PRESSING

Don't give up, even when you miss the mark and get out of step. Know the Holy Spirit is working in you. He is converting those "stations" in you that haven't yet been converted. Continue to remind yourself that as long as you are making steady progress, you are on the winning side. Stay in the line! Remain in formation! Heed the Holy Spirit's instructions!

Forget—don't dwell on—the mistakes you make. Instead, strain toward what lies ahead of you. Press on! Reach toward the goal of being completely controlled by the Spirit, so you can win the prize of living and walking in the Spirit (see Phil. 3:12–14).

Call to Action

1. What is one way you get out of line and stop walking in the Spirit?
2. What are (or were) some of your "full-power stations" that need to be (or were) converted?
3. What are (or were) some of your "low-power stations" that need to be (or were) converted?
4. Review the benefits of walking. What are the top three ways walking can benefit you personally? How will you increase your level of walking (for example, pace, time, hills)?
5. What action is God prompting you to take?

Thank You, Father, for being so patient with me. Thank You, too, for letting me know You love me and think highly of me even when I get off step. Thank You for knowing my heart. Please continue to change me so I become completely responsive to and controlled by the Spirit in regard to my eating. Help me live more under the Spirit's control with each passing day. Bless me always to be sensitive to sin and never to give myself a license to continue sinning. Even though I'll never see one hundred percent perfection in this life, put something in me that hates sin, loves righteousness, and presses toward the mark to win the heavenly prize every single day of my life. In Jesus' name I pray. Amen.

Strategy Six

RENEW YOUR MIND

Chapter 16

HEART MATTERS

THINGS IN MY life are so heavy right now, I want to turn to food to escape the pain. I know eating won't solve the problem and can only offer a temporary fix. It'll bring a short period of relief, but once the food digests, my stomach will be empty again.

When am I going to get past the desire to eat for comfort? God, I know You are the God of all comfort, and You can thoroughly comfort my heart. I'm sorry I continue to run to food instead of You. Thank You for allowing me to recognize this fault. Continue to change me and help me to press toward the mark of food no longer being a source of comfort in my life. Help me to run to You instead to settle all issues of my heart.

Create in me a clean heart, O God; and renew a right spirit within me.
—Psalm 51:10 KJV

A CLEAN HEART

This is my same old story (and maybe it's yours as well): "God, please change me." "God, please cleanse my heart." But it's true. I really do want a clean heart. Sometimes it seems like the closer I get in my relationship with God, the more flaws and filthiness I see within myself. It's as if the more I understand about His holiness, the more I see my unrighteousness. Can you relate? Do you desperately want to be holy but just can't seem to get there?

In our frustration, we can find consolation in God. He knew our shortcomings long before He created the world, which is why He sent His Son to make a way for us to be cleansed from all unrighteousness.

Any righteousness we possess comes from Jesus Christ. Because the Holy Spirit lives within us, we should want our temples—God's dwelling place—to be clean. We should want our hearts to be spiritually, physically, emotionally, morally, and ethically clean. We should want God to create—to shape—our hearts to be fashioned after His heart.

The Hebrew meaning of "heart" in Psalm 51:10 refers to the inner part that makes up a person—the soul, mind (knowledge, thinking, reflection, memory), inclination, determination of will, conscience, seat of appetites, seat of emotions and passions, and seat of courage.[1] If these areas are clean, especially in regard to food, we can know our thoughts, decisions, and actions will be clean, and we won't have to worry about whether what we are doing is right or wrong.

In that same verse, "a *right* spirit within me" means a spirit that is stable, established, fixed, secure, prepared, settled, and ready.[2] If our spirits are right, food will not move us.

The Hebrew meaning of "spirit" in Psalm 51:10 refers to vigor, courage, temper, amount of patience, disposition, impulse, desire, seat of moral character, seat of emotion, and energy of life.[3] David wrote Psalm 51 as a prayer for forgiveness and cleansing after the prophet Nathan came to him about his adultery with Bathsheba and the murder of her husband.

In verse 10, David asks God for purity. He wanted God to create a new heart in him because he knew purity couldn't come from what already existed within. We need to want what David wanted, because there are desires, impulses, and other ungodly parts of our spirits that are so dirty they need to be made completely new. If we possess a right spirit, we'll be able to resist temptation and not sin in the area of food.

HEART INSIGHTS

In his book *Waking the Dead*, John Eldredge says, "Our heart has been made good by the work of Christ, but we haven't learned how to live from it."[4] I agree with this to a point. When we accept Christ as our

Savior, our hearts undergo immediate change, and we are made "good," giving us right standing with God.

There are, however, unresolved issues (sins) hidden in our hearts, and we must be trained by the Holy Spirit to deal with these issues. We do so by walking with God.

Walking with God is the same as walking in the Spirit—keeping in line with the written Word and obeying and remaining in tune with the Holy Spirit who lives within us. When we do so, issues of the heart can be cleaned, made right, and renewed. Other issues are dealt with when God creates new emotions, thoughts, motivations, and actions in our hearts.

STAY OUT OF THE DIRT

God does the majority of the work as we are transformed, converted, and cleaned. Still, we have a part to play. We are responsible to listen to and obey what God tells us as we read the Bible and listen to the Holy Spirit, and to stay out of the dirt (sin)!

Kids love to play in the dirt. If we still enjoy playing in the dirt and making mud pies when we're thirty, that's a problem! Kids are expected to play in the dirt and get dirty. It's part of growing up. When we get older, however, we're expected to be more responsible. We are expected to behave in ways that enrich our lives and make them better.

Getting dirty and playing in the mud signifies our lives before we came to Christ. After salvation, we are expected to mature in Him. Signs of maturity include staying out of the dirt (sin), becoming more responsible, and being obedient to the Word and the Spirit.

KNOW YOUR ENEMY

Part of becoming mature in Christ means becoming more aware of our enemy. When we were children, our parents protected us from enemies. They taught us what to do in case they weren't around to protect us. They said things like "Don't talk to strangers" and "Never go anywhere with anyone you don't know."

As we grow up and become responsible for our own lives, we must be wary of the enemy. To do this, we must know our enemy, the devil.

You must know his characteristics so you can recognize him and his tactics.

The devil is an *enemy* (1 Pet. 5:8). He absolutely hates us. He devises sinister schemes to use against us. He is out to harm us. As our enemy, he is our opponent—our adversary—and he opposes us with deep-seated hostility.

The devil is a *tempter* (Matt. 4:1). He uses people and things to lure, entice, seduce, captivate, stimulate, and charm us to appeal to our senses and coax us to sin. He'll do anything to draw us into a wrong or foolish course of action.

The devil is a *slanderer* (Job 1:6–12). He speaks false and malicious statements against our reputations. He speaks lies to us about other people's reputations. He wants us to think badly about others, and others to think badly of us. He does everything he can to slander God's good name as well.

The devil is an *accuser* (Zech. 3:1; Rev. 12:10). He tempts us to do wrong, then eagerly awaits to accuse us. All day and all night, he seeks to charge us with a fault, offense, crime, shortcoming, or error. He even accuses God. He charges our faithful, loving, and giving Father of withholding things from us, not being a protector or provider, and neglecting, leaving, and forsaking us.

The devil is a *deceiver* (Gen. 3:1; 2 Cor. 11:14; 2 Thes. 2:9–10). He lies and cheats to get us to do his bidding. He tricks us into sinning. He deceptively leads us against what is true, right, and good. He is a counterfeit and disguises himself as something good. He masks himself and his tactics as something other than what they really are—weapons of destruction!

The devil is a *thief* and a *destroyer* (John 10:10). He is a master thief. He'll rob us right in front of our eyes! He's like a prowling lion and will steal from us secretly and slyly before we even know what hit us! He is a master demolitionist. He doesn't seek just to wound us. He aims to permanently tear down, thoroughly ruin, completely spoil, and utterly destroy. His ultimate goal is to annihilate the kingdom of God and to slaughter you and me, along with every believer in Christ.

GUARD YOUR HEART

Our enemy wants to destroy our hearts. As you recall, the heart is the inner part of your being that makes you, you. Guard your heart so the enemy cannot get to it.

- Protect your *mind* (knowledge, thinking, reflection, memory) by knowing and grounding yourself in the Word of God.
- Guard your *inclinations* by learning to like the things God likes.
- Protect your *determination of will* by taking action and deliberately choosing to do what is right in the eyes of God.
- Guard your *conscience* by letting the Holy Spirit and the Word guide all your decisions.
- Protect your *seat of appetites* by consulting the Holy Spirit for what and how much to eat instead of allowing what you eat to be dictated by your flesh. ("Seat of appetites" doesn't just refer to food but to any strong desire or craving.)
- Guard your *seat of emotions and passions* by obeying the Holy Spirit and the Word instead of going by what you want, think, or feel.
- Protect your *seat of courage* by refusing to give in to fear. Place your confidence in God and trust Him with your whole heart (Prov. 3:5–6).

Guarding our hearts is a serious matter, which is why God tells us in Proverbs 4:23 (NIV), "Above all else, guard your heart, for it is the wellspring of life." Notice we are told to guard our hearts "above all else." Why? Because our hearts are the source of who we are and what we think, say, and do. Jesus said, "A good person produces good things from the treasury of a good heart, and an evil person produces evil things from the treasury of an evil heart. What you say flows from what is in your heart" (Luke 6:45 NLT).

The level at which we protect or guard our hearts determines whether what comes out of us will be good or evil.

Also, if we don't take care of our spiritual and physical hearts, nothing else will be strong enough to withstand the spiritual and physical attacks of the enemy. Be mindful of your heart. Protect it by taking in spiritual nourishment daily through reading the Word, praying, and meditating. Get regular exercise and eat right to protect your heart physically. Don't be lax in protecting your heart; the devil is waiting for an opportunity to pounce and destroy!

RENEW YOUR MIND

Renewing our minds will help us to properly guard our hearts. "Renew" in Romans 12:2 means to willingly adjust our moral and spiritual vision and thinking to the mind of God.[5] This is something *we* must do. We are responsible for replacing worldly thinking with God's truth. The Holy Spirit will not do this for us the way He does other things, such as convict (John 16:8–11), guide us into truth (John 16:13), give spiritual gifts (1 Cor. 12:4–8), and produce fruit (Gal. 5:22–23).

As we properly respond to this adjustment, "an inward spiritual transformation takes place that makes [our] whole life new in its motives and ends."[6] We are renovated—completely changed for the better!

Knowing the enemy can also help us renew our minds. The more aware we are of his tactics and schemes, the easier it will be for us to resist him. Adjusting our moral and spiritual vision to the mind of God will help us withstand Satan. We must wholeheartedly seek to line up our ideals, mind-sets, goals, and desires to match God's thinking and plans for our lives if we hope to renew our minds to the mind (and heart) of God.

HEART PRAYERS

The best way to ensure a clean heart is to pray God's Word about it. We know God hears and answers our prayers (Isa. 65:24). Prayer makes things happen (James 5:16), and praying God's Word will help to bring to pass the purpose for which His Word was sent (Isa. 55:11).

Here are some examples of praying Scripture over our hearts.

Lord, help me to love You with all my heart, soul, and mind (Matt. 22:37).

Lord, please give me a new heart and put a new spirit within me. Take away my hardened heart and give me a heart that is sensitive and responsive to Your touch (Ezek. 11:19).

Father, guard my heart so I don't drift toward evil or take part in acts of wickedness. Don't let my heart be drawn to do wrong (Ps. 141:4).

Let the things I speak and the things I think about always be acceptable to You, Lord (Ps. 19:14).

Search me, O God, and reveal what's in my heart and in my thoughts. If there is anything wicked or offensive in me, please remove it and lead me down the right path to eternal life with You (Ps. 139:23–24).

There are many scriptures pertaining to the heart. Use a Bible concordance to find them, and then pray them. God *will* answer! If He sees your sincerity in the matter, He promises to answer (Ps. 37:4).

Do your part to keep your heart clean. Obey God and stay out of sin; know your enemy and resist him; renew your mind so your thinking becomes like God's; pray for a clean heart.

Call to Action

1. Which tactic of the enemy do you fall for most often?
2. Of the parts of the heart (listed under "Guard Your Heart"), which area in your heart do you need most to protect? Why do you think you are especially vulnerable in that area?
3. Find a Scripture verse you can pray that will help you with a current heart issue.
4. What action is God prompting you to take?

Lord, please help me to do my part to keep Your temple clean. Help me to fully obey You without hesitation. Help me to be thoroughly aware of the enemy and to resist him at the outset. Help my thoughts and ways to become like Yours. Create in me a clean heart, O God, and renew a loyal, unyielding spirit within me. In the name of Jesus, I pray. Amen.

Chapter 17

THE WAR IS ON!

*I*DECIDED TO *give myself a break from perfectionist tendencies by reducing my morning intake of spiritual nourishment. Normally, I read books, devotionals, Scripture, prayers, and other things. I thought I was doing myself a favor by spending less time reading so I could have more time for other responsibilities. Though I cut back, I thought I still gave myself enough spiritual food to sustain me.*

I was wrong. But I didn't realize how wrong until a week later when I weighed myself. Physically, I had gained about two pounds. Spiritually, I'd lost my ability to fight well. Neglecting to fill up on spiritual nourishment caused me to lose some battles with the enemy. All week I lost self-control, and my attitude was like Dr. Jekyll and Mr. Hyde. By week's end, I was so volatile I wanted to snap someone's head off!

Boy, was I deceived! What I thought was a voice looking out for my good was actually the voice of the enemy. The idea to take a break presented itself as thoughtful and caring. Underneath it all, shrewd cunning deceived me into positioning myself for defeat.

He who has no rule over his own spirit is like a city that is broken down and without walls.

—Proverbs 25:28 AMP

THE WAR

"It was the best of times, it was the worst of times, it was the age of wisdom, it was the age of foolishness, it was the epoch of belief, it was the epoch of incredulity, it was the season of Light, it was the season of Darkness ..."

So begins Charles Dickens's *A Tale of Two Cities*. It aptly describes the perpetual conflict we face as Christians. Whether or not we realize it, the duplicity of Satan, our chief adversary, is the culprit. He cleverly manipulates people and things to oppose what is good. As I mentioned in the previous chapter, we need to recognize our enemy to keep from ending up on his side. Knowing Truth—which is God—and everything we can about our enemy will help us choose rightly.

When I reduced my reading, I didn't recognize the enemy despite everything I know about him. He disguised himself so well that I fell for his scheme. I didn't make the connection between shorter morning devotions and having less self-control until I was like a city with broken-down walls, open to the attack of the enemy. We can't assume something is good just because it seems good or feels good.

Throughout the Bible we are admonished to be on guard. Like military watchmen, we are to stand guard and protect the things God puts in our care. Like it or not, we are enlisted in an invisible war: Satan versus God, evil versus good, natural versus spiritual.

SATAN VS. GOD

Satan wants to destroy you and wants you to receive his same end—separation from God and eternal punishment. God wants to give you life and eternal blessings. He sent His Son to provide the way for you to escape what you deserved—separation and punishment, the due penalty for your sins.

Satan hates you with such intensity that he'll do everything he can to get you to sin and miss out on God's blessings. Jesus loves you with such fervor that He'll do whatever it takes to deliver you from sin and bless you. He willingly left the splendor of heaven and the throne of His glory to die for you. His death made it possible for you to receive the ultimate blessings—forgiveness of sins and eternal life.

Satan uses deceitful tactics and schemes to fool you into believing he is for you when he's not. He disguises himself in order to trick you into going against God. You can be sure he's in the midst when you experience pain, loss, sickness, or tragedy.

God operates aboveboard. He openly shows His love for you. He displays His deep affection all around you and gives you your senses to enjoy it. You can *see* His love in the way He carefully sculpted this magnificent earth. You can *feel* it when you experience things like love, peace, and joy. You can *touch* it when you give or receive a loving embrace. You can *taste* it when you eat delicious food. And you can *hear* it through music and words that touch your heart.

Who has the upper hand in your life—Satan or God?

EVIL VS. GOOD

When God created the world, it was good. Satan, being God's enemy, hates all that is good, so he deceived Eve in order to expose the world to evil. God created people to enjoy the earth, and for relationship. Satan is behind the destruction of relationships, marriages, families, and homes.

God is good; there is no evil in Him. Satan is evil; there is no good in him. God wants to give you good things that bless and satisfy you. Satan wants to give you evil things that curse you and leave you lacking and unfulfilled. God wants to give you health, vitality, and longevity. Satan wants you weak, sick, and perishing. God is blameless, fair, pure, safe, stable, and loyal. Satan is guilty, unfair, corrupt, dangerous, fickle, and disloyal. Everything good is from God; everything that isn't can be attributed to Satan.

What do you experience most often—evil or good?

NATURAL VS. SPIRITUAL

Natural refers to anything we can see with our eyes and hear with our ears, as well as things we can smell, taste, and touch. Our senses don't always accurately judge spiritual matters. Spiritual things such as God and Satan, angels and demons, and good and evil exist in an invisible realm.

We react to the natural world by what we experience with our physical bodies. If something looks right or makes us feel good, we tend to gravitate toward it. Entering a relationship with a good-looking person, hearing words that sound good, eating foods that taste good, or engaging in activities because they make us feel good doesn't mean they are good.

Upon further investigation, we may find that good-looking person we thought was so wonderful wants nothing to do with God and desires to keep us from Him, too. Those words that sounded so sincere are really lies. The food that tasted good now is actually clogging your arteries, leading you to an early grave. And the things that felt so good—sexual immorality, greed, drunkenness, anger, divisions, sorcery, wild parties, addictions, and so forth—are an abomination to God (Col. 3:5; Gal. 5:19–21).

Although we live in a natural world, spiritual forces are at work all around us. We can't see what's happening in the spiritual world, but it greatly influences the natural one. Some of these forces war for God (2 Kings 6:16–17; Ps. 34:7; 91:11; Heb. 1:14) and others against Him (Dan. 10:12–13; Eph. 6:12). Knowing this should cause us to examine every situation for which side is at work—evil or good. Responding appropriately to the impact of the spiritual world on our circumstances in this natural world can keep us from making wrong choices.

Which world has greater impact on your decisions—the natural or the spiritual?

Natural vs. spiritual self. When we make decisions, we either follow our natural self or our spiritual self. According to 1 Corinthians 2:14, the natural self does not receive the things of the Spirit of God. The natural self considers God's ways and God's directions foolishness. It cannot understand God, nor can it receive spiritual things because it is led by its senses. It is driven by what it wants, thinks, and feels and is ruled by thoughts, physical needs, and desires. The natural self is an enemy to God (Rom. 5:10).

The spiritual self is led by God's Spirit and not the senses. The spiritual self desires to follow the will of God. Following our spiritual selves will lead us to righteousness and victory.

Which self most often leads you—the natural or the spiritual?

Natural vs. spiritual appetite. We either surrender to our natural appetites or to our spiritual appetites. The natural appetite refers to the desire for things we want to have or experience, such as (but not limited to) food, drink, possessions, or pleasure. The spiritual appetite refers to the desire for things God wants us to have and experience, such as peace, love, joy, and forgiveness. Our spiritual appetites can only be filled by submission to the Holy Spirit. Seeking to appease our natural appetites with natural things and neglecting to fill our spiritual appetites with the things of God will eventually lead to death.

Which appetite do you fill most often—the natural or the spiritual?

THE FLESH

The voice of our flesh speaks through our senses. The flesh is vocal, boisterous, rude, and pushy. Because this voice is so "loud," it can easily deceive us into thinking it's the right voice to follow. Our flesh's senses are extremely greedy. The invisible force in the power of its will coerces us to go along with it. Left unchecked, its naturally voracious appetite can easily be manipulated by Satan. He uses the wants, desires, and cravings of our flesh to get us to sin. The flesh doesn't care about consequences; they don't matter. It only cares about getting its way. It cannot say no to itself—it doesn't want to! The flesh says things like "It's OK to have sex with your significant other because you're getting married eventually"; "Cheat on your income tax because you pay too much anyway"; "Get the extra-large meal"; "Give me ____ and give it to me *now!*" The flesh will lead us to destruction without a second thought.

How often do you give in to your flesh?

THE SPIRIT

The Holy Spirit speaks to our spirits (Rom. 8:14, 16). He speaks to our understanding, or the inner awareness of our hearts, by giving us wisdom, revelation, and knowledge (Eph. 1:17–18). He doesn't speak to our senses. He speaks that which aligns with the Word of God. The Spirit is soft-spoken, gentle, and humble (1 Kings 19:11–13). He knows what is right, and He quietly tells us, yet He won't force us to follow Him. He is one with God; therefore, He cannot be manipulated by

Satan. He cares about what's best for us and wants to lead us toward righteousness. He says things like "Choose fruit instead of dessert"; "Forgive that person who hurt you"; "Trust me to help you instead of doing something immoral"; "What would Jesus do in this situation?" He is well aware of consequences and is deeply hurt when we make wrong choices.

How often do you obey the Holy Spirit?

LIFE OR DEATH

Notice what it says in Romans 8:13 (NIV): "For if you live according to the sinful nature, you will die; but if by the Spirit you put to death the misdeeds of the body, you will live" and in Galatians 6:8 (NIV): "The one who sows to please his sinful nature, from that nature will reap destruction; the one who sows to please the Spirit, from the Spirit will reap eternal life." These verses clearly state that if we live by the sinful nature, we'll be destroyed, and if we are led by the Spirit we will live.

Galatians 5:19–21 (NLT) reiterates this truth. It also lists some of the acts of the sinful nature: "sexual immorality, impurity, lustful pleasures, idolatry, sorcery, hostility, quarreling, jealousy, outbursts of anger, selfish ambition, dissension, division, envy, drunkenness, wild parties," along with several other deeds. If you are partaking of any of these behaviors, turn from doing them and toward God so your sins can be wiped out (Acts 3:19).

In order to put to death the deeds of the body (the sinful nature) and overcome the world, we must rely on the Holy Spirit to empower us to turn away from sin. It isn't easy, but it's doable. We can make it happen by getting to know God and His voice. We can get to know Him by spending time in His Word and in prayer, and by setting our minds on Him—focusing on Him and seeking Him constantly.

FIGHT TO WIN!

We are in a tug-of-war. God is pulling us toward Him, and Satan is pulling us toward him. Every decision we make either builds God's side or builds Satan's. The choices we make strengthen either the side of good or the side of evil. We vacillate, sometimes obeying our sinful nature and other times obeying the Spirit. When we choose to submit our wills to God, we end up on the winning side. When we surrender to Satan by yielding to sin, we're led to a great loss.

Popular belief says opposites attract. I am here to tell you that when it comes to God and Satan, good and evil, spiritual and natural, opposites *do not* attract! This war will end with either life or death. Be aware and always be on guard!

Call to Action

1. Do you live more on the natural or spiritual side of things? How do you know?
2. What can you do to live more on the spiritual side?
3. What do you do that leads to life?
4. What do you do that leads to death?
5. What action is God prompting you to take?

Lord, help me to take this battle seriously. Keep me mindful that I'm in a war, and help me to be on guard. Help me to know my enemy better. Help me to recognize him and not fall for his schemes. Help me to listen intently for Your gentle voice. Teach me to hear You. Clean the wax from my spiritual ears, remove the walls from my heart, and penetrate my soul with an ever-increasing filling of You. Let nothing get between me and You—especially not this world, my flesh, or sin. In Jesus' name I pray. Amen.

Chapter 18

WHAT'S EATING YOU?

I ATE DINNER *before heading to a meeting. Three hours later while on our way home, my husband asked what I wanted to eat. Automatically, I started thinking about what to eat. I didn't think about whether I was hungry. I was out with my husband, and for the past two weeks eating out had been our entertainment.*

We ended up at Big Dogg's, a newly built hotdog stop. We spotted it as we drove past. My husband made a U-turn to get to it. I got so excited about the variety of hot dogs and hamburgers on the menu that it never crossed my mind I wasn't hungry. I spotted Italian turkey sausage on the menu. I told my husband to order that and we could split it. (Thinking back, something good was working in the midst of my mindlessness for me to choose the turkey sausage and to want to split it.) My husband was glad about my offer, yet he ordered a "meal deal" that came with two hotdogs and two orders of fries.

When we got home, we put on a movie. I plopped in front of the TV and dumped part of an order of fries and half the turkey sausage on my plate. When I finished eating, my stomach felt overly full and uncomfortable. As I sat there moaning and rubbing my belly, it finally registered: not only had I eaten dinner a few hours prior, but in that short sitting, without even thinking, I had polished off half a hotdog, some fries, a fairly large cookie, and some leftover cinnamon popcorn. I was totally disconnected from everything I'd eaten.

My mind was disengaged when I decided to get something to eat, and it was disengaged when I ate while watching TV. When I did start thinking, it was too late. By that time I was miserable and remorseful. In my mindless eating, my flesh reared its ugly head.

And that they may come to their senses [and] escape out of the snare of the devil, having been held captive by him, [henceforth] to do His [God's] will.

—2 Timothy 2:26 AMP

MINDLESS EATING

The devil hooked me when I received the initial invitation to eat. He baited me with something so simple, and I fell right into his trap! In my mindless stupor, I neglected to be on guard, which gave Satan easy access. Had it not been for the warning system God built into our bodies, there's no telling how far I would have gone, but feeling miserably full brought me to my senses. I had fallen hook, line, and sinker and consequently dishonored my temple by overindulging in food.

Mindlessness is a work of the flesh. The flesh doesn't think about end results, nor does it care about consequences. It cares only about fulfilling its desires. Mindless eating can fall into three categories: (1) not thinking about whether we are hungry, (2) not thinking about what we are eating, and (3) not thinking about the amount we eat.

Not thinking about whether we are hungry can lead to eating as a source of comfort or escape or eating to fulfill cravings, tastes, and desires. Not thinking about what we are eating can lead to making unhealthy food choices. Not thinking about the amount we eat usually leads to overeating, possibly even binge eating, and ultimately weight gain. I realize there are some people who don't think about eating and don't eat enough. Eating too much or too little is a sin. We are to take care of our bodies by giving them what they need, nothing more and nothing less.

To avoid mindless eating, ask yourself these three questions before you eat:

1. Am I hungry? (Do I need to eat?)
2. What should I eat?
3. How much should I eat?

If the answer to the first question is no, don't eat. We must take charge over our flesh and refuse to let it have its way. People with certain conditions or diseases, such as diabetes, need to eat more often. In this case, the better question would be, do I *need* to eat? If you need to eat because of low blood sugar or low energy levels, then eat, but eat what will benefit your body.

When answering the second question, we need to think about the nutrients our bodies need. We all need nutrients from the five major food groups—grains, vegetables, fruits, milk, and meat and protein—to help our bodies run properly. God created a wide variety of foods for us to choose from so we can get the nutrients we need. The better we provide for our bodies, the better they will run.

To answer the last question, we must be in tune with our bodies. Every body is different, so there is no set rule. For example, some people function better with more grains and less meat and protein; others need lots of meat and protein and a small amount of fruit; others need mostly vegetables and less of everything else. Not only that, some people need to eat larger amounts, while others need smaller amounts. The key is to be aware of the needs of your body and how it responds to the foods you eat.

Listen to your body. If a food (and the amount you eat) is right for you, you'll feel good. If not, you won't. I highly recommend praying about what and how much to eat and listening to the Holy Spirit for guidance.

EAT A VARIETY

God created a wide variety of foods for us to enjoy and for the nourishment of our bodies. In the United States, food is divided into five main groups. Let's look at each group to help us better understand what to eat and the nutrients our bodies need. As I stated earlier, the five major food groups are grains, vegetables, fruits, milk, and meat and protein.

Grains include breads, cereals, rice, and pasta. Grains provide complex carbohydrates, vitamins, minerals, and fiber. Carbohydrates provide the easiest source of energy for our bodies to use. Vitamins and minerals help our bodies work properly. Although vitamins and minerals naturally occur in grains, processing removes them. You will notice the words *enriched* or *fortified* on some packages. This means the vitamins and minerals lost during processing were added back in so their helpful benefits wouldn't stay lost. Fiber helps to prevent constipation and helps reduce the risk of certain diseases.[1]

Like grains, both the fruit and the vegetable groups provide vitamins, minerals, and fiber, but to a much higher degree. Researchers have identified compounds in fruits and vegetables called phytochemicals that contain protective, disease-preventing compounds.[2] Studies have shown these properties prevent diseases such as cancer, diabetes, cardiovascular disease, and hypertension. Different colors of fruits and vegetables contain different phytochemicals, which provide various health benefits. To get maximum health benefits from fruits and vegetables, eat a variety of colors.

Foods in the milk group include milk, cheese, cottage cheese, ricotta cheese, yogurt, and tofu. This group provides calcium and protein. Calcium is important for healthy bones, teeth, heart, muscles, nerves, and blood.[3] It is one of the most vital minerals for optimal functioning of the entire body.

Even if you don't eat or drink dairy products, be sure you are getting enough calcium from other sources like dark green leafy vegetables such as broccoli and greens. The soft bones found in canned sardines or salmon are a good source of calcium too. You can also drink calcium-fortified orange juice or "milks" like rice, almond, coconut, or soy milk. (I recommend eating and drinking soy products in moderation due to the negative affect they may have on your hormones and your health.)

The meat and protein group includes poultry, seafood, eggs, nuts, nut butters, seeds, and beans. These foods are important because they provide proteins, the basic building blocks of skin, muscles, and organs. Animal protein, the most complete protein, contains all the essential amino acids our bodies need.[4] Many foods in this group also contain iron, which makes it possible for our blood to carry oxygen throughout our bodies. If you do not eat meat, be sure to get protein from other sources such as nuts, nut butters, seeds, and legumes.

(For more easy-to-follow information on food groups, go to www. choosemyplate.gov.)

BALANCE YOUR ENERGY

To help us best decide how much to eat, we must first understand what calories are. A calorie is a unit of *energy* supplied by food.[5] The amount of energy supplied depends on what we eat. Proteins and carbohydrates contain four calories, or units of energy, per gram. Fats contain nine calories, or units of energy, per gram. (Notice for every gram of fat we eat, we consume more than twice as many calories as a gram of protein or carbohydrate!)

Our bodies need calories, or energy, to function. Our bodies need energy to help them perform automatic functions like breathing, maintaining body temperature, and keeping our hearts beating. We also need energy to perform activities like thinking, sitting, moving, walking, and anything else that helps our bodies operate.

The more we move about, the more calories we need to eat to provide our bodies with the energy they need to sustain that movement. In other words, if we move a little and sit a lot, we need to eat fewer calories. If we stand more than sit and move around at a moderate pace for a sustained period of time, we need more calories. If we are constantly moving and are doing things that get our hearts beating faster, we need even more calories to provide us with the necessary energy to sustain our activities.

Generally speaking, if you have a mostly *inactive* lifestyle in which you get thirty minutes or less of physical activity each day, you need to eat fewer calories because you are using little energy. If you are *moderately active* and get anywhere between thirty and sixty minutes of physical activity each day, you need a moderate amount of calories. If you are *active* and get sixty minutes or more of physical activity each day, you need a greater number of calories to sustain your active lifestyle.

Please note, I'm *not* encouraging you to count calories. I've included this information only to help you understand the correlation between food, exercise, and weight. I personally don't count calories because for me it's a form of bondage. Instead, I monitor my food intake, keep track of my daily steps using a pedometer, and track the amount of physical activity I get each week.

ENERGY IN, ENERGY OUT

To further explain the concept of how to balance our energy—the energy we consume in calories and the energy we use in activity—think about a two-sided balance scale. How we balance energy determines whether we maintain, gain, or lose weight.

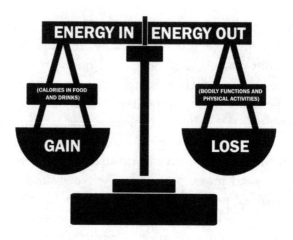

To *maintain* our current body weight, the calories we consume must be roughly equal to the calories we use in physical activity. Said another way, energy in equals equal energy out. To lose or gain weight, we need to tip the scale in one direction or the other. To *gain* weight, we eat more calories than we use and we're less active—more energy in and less energy out. To *lose* weight, we eat fewer calories than we use and we're more active—less energy in and more energy out.

PITFALLS

Knowing what and how much to eat is only part of the story of what influences our food intake. How we feel also impacts our eating. From a Humana-sponsored program called Weight No More, I learned the acronym HALT to help prevent certain feelings from being triggers for

146

wanting to eat. HALT is a reminder not to allow ourselves to get too Hungry, Angry, Lonely, and Tired.

Now when I know I'm not hungry, I investigate what I'm feeling and wanting by asking myself questions like these: What am I feeling right now? Am I mad? Tired? Lonely? What do I need right now? A hug? A break? Companionship? This helps me identify what's behind wanting to eat when I'm not really hungry.

I've also learned to avoid SOBS—feeling Stressed, Overwhelmed, Burdened, and Shaken. I made up this acronym because I often found myself feeling these things, and for me they triggered mindless eating. When I felt these emotions, instead of seeking the Lord for help and strength, I sought food. I've since learned to go to God when I feel SOBS.

HALT and SOBS can lead to mindless eating, overeating, and weight gain, which is why God wants us to halt our sobs (pun intended). Buckling under the pressure when we feel HALT or losing faith when we feel SOBS gives the world a bad impression of God. It's hard for unbelievers to imagine God as a helper when His children react negatively to HALT and SOBS. Our reaction also makes it seem as if God is not trustworthy or dependable.

We need to change our outlook. The solution to HALT SOBS is found in His Word.

Hungry. Food offers only temporary satisfaction (Matt. 4:4). *Spiritual sustenance is lasting.*

Angry. Don't sin in your anger (Eph. 4:26). *Handle your anger properly.*

Lonely. God will never leave you (Heb. 13:5). *He will help you face challenges successfully.*

Tired. Don't get tired of doing what's right (Gal. 6:9). *Trust God. Good will eventually come.*

Stressed. Don't worry about anything (Phil. 4:6). *Pray, talk to God, and wait confidently for His answer.*

Overwhelmed. Nothing is too hard for God (Gen. 18:14). *Ask Him to help you.*

Burdened. Cast your burdens on the Lord (Ps. 55:22). *Don't keep them. He wants to bear them for you.*

Shaken. Don't be shaken (Acts 2:25). *The Lord is right beside you.*

God is our Father. He wants to help us. He wants to save us. The problem is we don't seek Him for help. He's waiting. All we have to do is ask and then let Him work.

LIVE WITH INTENTION

The only way to subdue the problems of the flesh is by living with intention. Purpose to do God's will and please Him in *everything* you do. The flesh will attempt to overrule your decision through mindlessness, habits, and self-gratification, but fight against this. Follow the voice of the all-knowing Holy Spirit. He knows how to help you and what is best for you. If you seek Him and do what He says, He'll lead you along the path of righteousness, holiness, self-control, and blessing.

Here are some of the things I've done to practice living with intention.

- Before doing anything, ask, "Father, what would You have me do?"
- Go on a thirty-day fast, denying yourself at least one fleshly pleasure and implementing something to help you focus more on God (for example, no TV, avoid sugary treats, add additional Bible-reading time, do a spiritual workbook study on a specific topic).
- Keep a daily log of an area you need to monitor (your relationship with God, how you spend your time, food and activity, for example). Develop a system to help you stay on track. Refer to the appendix for help. (This idea was sparked from using the *Fearless Living Daily Training Manual* by Rhonda Britten for three months.)
- Plan your day—how you will spend your time and what you will eat. (Consult God first!)
- Take evaluation breaks. At intervals throughout your day, evaluate the things you've done for what was fleshly and what was spiritual.

- Develop a chart of habits you want to start or stop, and for thirty days keep track of how you do. (This idea was sparked from reading *30 Days to Taming Your Tongue* and *30 Days to Taming Your Stress* by Deborah Smith Pegues.)
- Meditate on different scriptures to live by. Try Joshua 1:9, Proverbs 3:5–6, Luke 6:27–28, Ephesians 4:32, Philippians 4:6, Colossians 3:18–21, or 1 Thessalonians 5:16–18 for starters.
- Ask God to show you what to work on and a monitoring system for it.

We must be intentionally thoughtful and aware. We cannot go through life mindlessly, or we'll end up living by the world's standards, being ruled by our flesh, and falling for Satan's lies. To live God-honoring lives, we must live purposefully and with holy intention, choosing to follow His standards and plan found in His Word, the Bible.

Call to Action

1. What percentage of your day do you usually spend in mindless or habitual activity?
2. How might you be more aware each day?
3. Are you getting the results you want from the energy you put in your body and the energy that comes out? If not, what change(s) do you need to make?
4. Identify one of your pitfalls. What is a Scripture verse that can help you combat this difficulty?
5. What important nutrients are lacking in your diet? How will you get the proper amounts?
6. What action is God prompting you to take?

Father, in the name of Jesus, help me to be aware of what I'm doing at all times. Let me not live mindlessly, but help me live fully engaged and intentionally seeking Your will at all times and in all areas. Take away my mindless, thoughtless, robotic ways and help me to be intentional, thoughtful, and purposeful. In Jesus' name I pray. Amen.

Strategy Seven

ESTABLISH YOURSELF AS GOOD, ACCEPTABLE, AND PERFECT

Chapter 19

ESTABLISH YOURSELF

I DON'T ALWAYS realize the changes I've undergone until God points them out to me. He brings things to my mind to encourage me when I feel I'm not doing enough. Recently, I was feeling down on myself for not having perfected my eating and weight, when God reminded me of what had happened two weeks earlier.

My cousin was back in town for a visit after her recent move to Arizona, and she invited me to go to a Zumba class with her. After the class, I found out the instructor and another participant were her former co-workers and also that they had prearranged to get ice cream after the session. Since I had ridden with my cousin, I had no choice but to go.

In the "old days," before God changed me, I would've treated myself for working out. I was a junk-food junkie. When my cousin offered to pay, I would have jumped at the opportunity to enjoy a free treat! I liked eating and socializing; most of my social gatherings centered around food. And I would have gone crazy sampling most of the flavors and still purchased a cupful of ice cream plus toppings!

I no longer reward myself with food after working out. I turn down lots of junk-food offers. I enjoy socializing without needing to eat. When I go to ice cream shops, I sample only a few flavors. And I usually fill my cup less than half full and get very few toppings, if any!

I'm proud (and grateful to the Lord) to think I passed up ice cream even when I had so many reasons for getting some. I'm even prouder realizing I didn't have to talk myself out of it! My decision was firm from the beginning! I wanted the ice cream, but I wanted to feel well more than I wanted a snack.

I sat at the yogurt shop and enjoyed the company, the break, and the outdoors while everyone else enjoyed their ice cream. I didn't feel deprived or out of place the slightest bit. God has changed me—heart, mind, and body, and I thank Him for what He's done.

> Every good gift and every perfect gift is from above, and comes down from the Father of lights, with whom there is no variation or shadow of turning.
>
> —James 1:17 NKJV

GOOD AND PERFECT GIFTS

I studied the word "gift" in James 1:17 and discovered the two references to "gift" refer to different things. According to the *James, Faucet, and Brown Commentary on the Whole Bible*, the good gift denotes the act of giving or the gift in its beginning stage. The perfect gift refers to the thing given or the blessing or benefit coming from the gift.[1]

Next, I studied the words "good" and "perfect." I was surprised to find out these are the same Greek words used in Romans 12:2: "that you may prove what is that *good* and acceptable and *perfect* will of God" (emphasis mine).

God's good and perfect gifts are evident in my everyday life. His good gift allowed me to see how I had defiled my temple and sparked a desire in me to want to change. His perfect gift changed my nature, function, and condition. He changed my nature so that I now live to be healthy and pleasing to Him. He changed my function so that now I willingly choose to do what benefits my body instead of what feels or tastes good. He changed my condition so that now I'm healthier, more fit, and able to be more active. I'm grateful for God's good and perfect gifts, because the resulting blessings make me more like Him. And I know if He changed me, He can change you as well. He's waiting to rain His good and perfect gifts on you. Will you accept them?

PROVE IT!

Even though God gives us good and perfect gifts, we must do our part in becoming more like Him. Romans 12:2 says, "That *you* may prove" (emphasis mine). *We* are to prove something. To prove is to establish something as truthful or genuine, or to establish the quality or worth of something by testing it.

I believe Romans 12:2 gives us the following two tasks: (1) to establish *ourselves* as good, acceptable, and perfect, and (2) to establish our *choices* and *behavior* as good, acceptable, and perfect. (For the remainder of this chapter, I'm going to refer to choices and behavior as CAB.)

Before we can establish ourselves as good, acceptable, and perfect, we must examine our hearts. Are our hearts' desires good? Do they align with the Word of God? Is there evidence of the goodness and righteousness of God in our hearts? Are the motivations of our hearts honorable? Do we obey God? Do we follow the leading of the Holy Spirit? Are our hearts pure? Sincere?

We can say we've established ourselves as good, acceptable, and perfect if we can answer yes to each question in the previous paragraph. (No one is perfect, so it's impossible to answer yes one hundred percent of the time, but we should be making progress toward purity of heart.) If we cannot answer yes to every question, we must look at what we need to fix, change, or surrender.

Once we've established ourselves as good, acceptable, and perfect, we need to establish, or prove, whether our CAB is good, acceptable, and perfect. "Prove" in the Greek means to test, examine, or scrutinize something to see whether it is genuine or true to what it claims to be. If we profess to be believers in Christ, our CAB should prove to be genuine, true, and good. Check by measuring your CAB against the teachings in the Bible.

Every CAB should pass the following three tests: (1) Is it good? (2) Is it acceptable? (3) Is it perfect? Passing only one is not enough.

IS IT GOOD?

Is the CAB you plan to make good? Good in this case refers to the nature (the makeup or essence) of a thing. Check the nature of your CAB by asking, What is its nature? Is it contrary to God? Is it good, upright, or honorable? Is it wholesome? Is it beneficial? Is it advantageous? Does it promote health? Is it appropriate or fitting? Is it of the highest quality, rank, rate, or class? How is it useful to God?

If any part of the CAB is bad, dishonorable, unwholesome, or inappropriate or goes against God in any way, avoid it.

Some things by nature are neither good nor bad, honorable nor dishonorable. If this is the case, go to the next test and evaluate the CAB in a specific context. For the sake of illustration, let's relate the first test to a slice of cheesecake. The nature of cheesecake is neither good nor bad, and its essence is neither honorable nor dishonorable. By itself, it doesn't go against God. On some occasions, eating cheesecake may dishonor your health; other times, it may not. It's impossible to ascertain whether the cheesecake is good (for you) without looking at other factors, so let's proceed to the next test.

IS IT ACCEPTABLE?

The first test checked the nature of a CAB. For the second test, the *judgment* test, you must judge whether or not the CAB is acceptable for *you*.

Judge a CAB by asking: Is this agreeable to my body and/or my life? Will it be well pleasing to God for me to do? Is it sufficient or suitable? Will I be happy about my decision in the future? Will it yield negative or unpleasant consequences? Does it cause me to sin in any way? Does it go against anything in the Bible?

Relate this test again to the cheesecake. We learned from the first test the nature of cheesecake isn't bad. Now let's appraise whether it's acceptable for you. Don't eat the cheesecake if you've reached your sugar limit for the day, or if any additional sugar will cause you to feel unwell. In either case, eating it would not be good stewardship of your health (Luke 16:1–2; 1 Cor. 4:1–2).

You also may need to skip the cheesecake if you've already had some (or some other dessert). For you, more dessert might be gluttony, which the Bible warns against (Prov. 23:20–21). Also, eating it because you can't turn it down shows a lack of self-control, which is also a sin (2 Tim. 3:1–5). In these cases the acceptable thing is to avoid the cheesecake.

On the other hand, it may be OK to eat the cheesecake if you exercise regularly, make consistently healthy food choices, eat reasonable portions, are healthy, and usually practice self-control.

This test is individualized. It assesses a CAB relative to individual situations. What may be OK for one person is not necessarily right for someone else. What may be OK one day may not be OK the next. If the CAB is acceptable, move to the final test, which tests the *outcome* to see if the CAB will bring you closer to, or away from, perfection or maturity.

IS IT PERFECT?

This test will ensure a favorable outcome. God's will is that we become perfect, or complete, in Him. The Greek word for "perfect" is *teleios*, which means "that which has reached its end; nothing more to complete it."[2] God wants us to grow and become spiritually and morally mature (Luke 2:52; James 1:4; Heb. 5:12–14). Our CABs should lead to maturity in Christ Jesus.

Mature Christians possess discernment and sound judgment. They also progress in their spiritual lives. In time, they become more and more like Christ. Spiritually immature Christians have a shortfall in these areas. In order to grow from immature to mature Christians, we need to learn discernment and sound judgment through studying the Bible. We need to train our consciences, senses, minds, and bodies to distinguish good from evil.[3]

Check whether a CAB is perfect (for you) by asking, Will it help me grow spiritually? Will I become more complete? Is it necessary for me? Is it compromising in any way? Will it cause a setback or cause me to remain stagnant? Will it move me forward to maturity? If I do it, will I become more, or less, like Christ?

Let's return to the cheesecake for this final test. If having the cheesecake ignites sugar cravings or causes you to resort to old habits and behaviors, leave it alone. If you can eat it with no emotional, physical, or spiritual repercussions, then have at it! Perhaps God provided the cheesecake as a way to bless you because He knows you like it. If this is the case, it will pass all three tests, because God never contradicts himself.

A good, acceptable, and perfect CAB has no problem fitting into the will of God. It will not go against God's commands or precepts, and your final decision will somehow glorify Him. Not only that, it will benefit you and possibly others as well.

These three tests can help you with anything, not just food. Use them to test social activities, relationships, employment, clothing, entertainment—you name it! Measuring everything against God's standards will help you make right choices and establish yourself as good, acceptable, and perfect. Don't, however, get caught up on using these exact questions. They aren't set in stone. They're merely guides.

GET TUNED

We check whether a CAB is good, acceptable, and perfect because some things harm our spirits and/or our bodies, while other things energize and strengthen us. We must know what does what. If we are unsure, we can consult the Holy Spirit, who lives within us.

God designed our bodies to warn us when they're troubled. Some people, however, ignore the warnings. It is up to you to recognize warning signs, identify root causes, and do something about them. When it comes to eating, you may need to omit or add things from your diet, stop combining certain food groups during the same meal or start combining others, or eat less of some foods and more of others.

Eating things that aren't the best for you can cause a number of unpleasant problems—from gas to serious diseases like heart disease and diabetes. Eating properly solves many health problems. Minor discomforts like bloating and major problems like inflammatory bowel diseases such as Crohn's and irritable bowel syndrome can be managed successfully through diet.[4]

Warning signs are built into our spirits as well. Everyone has a conscience, although some people are more in tune to it than others. According to the *Student Bible Dictionary*, the conscience is an "awareness or sense that an action or attitude is right or wrong." It's that gut feeling that nudges you about what or what not to do. If you don't train yourself to hear it, you will ignore or miss it.

According to an *NIV Study Bible* note, the conscience is reliable when it is strengthened by the Holy Spirit. Paul referenced this truth in Romans 9:1 (NIV) when he wrote, "I speak the truth in Christ—I am not lying, my conscience confirms it through the Holy Spirit." Strengthen your conscience by absorbing and obeying the Word and by following the leading of the Holy Spirit.

Being grounded in the Word of God causes spiritual awareness to become part of our nature. The more in tune we are to the Word, the more powerful the Holy Spirit will be within us, and the more audible our conscience will be.

If you don't know your body, hear your conscience, or listen to the Holy Spirit, you won't be sure whether you are being told "Yes, do this" or "No, stop doing that."

HOW TO GET TUNED

We aren't automatically tuned in to our bodies or consciences, the Word, or the Holy Spirit. Getting in tune requires work on our part.

Pray

Ask God to show you what and what not to do for every decision you make. Ask Him to help you be sensitive to His leading through your body's cues, your conscience, the Word, and the Holy Spirit.

Listen

Listen to what your body is telling you. If you experience any unpleasant symptoms (gas, inflammation, pain, etc.), evaluate your diet and ask God to show you the culprit.

Listen to what your conscience is telling you. Have you ever heard a small voice tell you to do or not do something? Have you had a gut feeling about something? Have you ever felt relieved when you listened to that voice inside you, or regretted when you didn't? Think back to what the warning voice sounded like. That's the voice you want to be in tune with. That voice was either your conscience or the Holy Spirit. The voice will only become clearer the more you practice heeding its warnings. The Holy Spirit and/or your conscience will warn you of things, such as an increase in sinful behavior, apathy toward the things of God, a decline in the time you spend with God, or a loosening of your morals and values.

Learn

Learn everything you can about the problems you experience. Keeping a journal or log will assist you in this process. Pay special attention to lifestyle and behavior changes, emotional and hormonal changes, and anything else that comes to mind that can help you identify the problem. Be aware of when problems arise, efforts that work and those that don't, when problems go away, and what, if anything, contributed to their disappearance. Research all things related to the problems you experience. This will help you get to the root causes. Don't forget to use your Bible as a resource. Listening and learning will take time, so be patient.

Practice

Once you've identified a problem and its source, take the necessary steps to make things better by putting what you learn into practice. You may need to stop doing some things and start doing others, or reduce some things and increase others. Don't expect to change overnight. I've heard it said it takes at least twenty-one days to form a habit. I believe you need to stick with new behaviors anywhere from one to three months before they become ingrained.

Remember, no two people are exactly alike, so focus on *you* and what *your* body is telling you. God made everyone's body special and unique. Your body will tell you what it does and doesn't need. God made it that way! Listen to it.

Some things may be hidden and not so easy to find, but don't give up. Persevere. God will help you make the correlation. Just don't stop asking and seeking His help. More important, don't stop listening intently for what He (and your body) has to say.

Discipline and control your body. Force it to live in holiness and honor (1 Cor. 9:27; 1 Thes. 4:4.) Living and walking in the Spirit will assure your ability to prove what is God's good, acceptable, and perfect will.

Call to Action

1. What are some good and perfect gifts God has recently given you?
2. What is one thing you can do to establish *yourself* as good, acceptable, and perfect?
3. What is one thing you can do to establish your *choices and behavior* as good, acceptable, and perfect?
4. What can you do to be more in tune with your body and your spirit?
5. What action is God prompting you to take?

Lord, I thank You for giving me good and perfect gifts. You never shortchange me, yet I often shortchange myself. Help me to desire the best for my life the way You desire the best for me. Ignite a passion within me that seeks to do the very best I can to please You at all times. Let me not settle for anything less than what is best, and let me not press toward anything less than the mark of perfection. Change my heart so I proudly walk in integrity, honor, holiness, and maturity. Bless me to represent You well! In Jesus' name I pray. Amen.

Chapter 20

CONCLUDING TRUTHS

*E*ARLY IN MY *Romans 12:1–2 journey, I decided to take a weekend break from healthy eating. This decision was based on hearing others talk about how they "treated themselves" on the weekends. Every day leading up to the weekend, I daydreamed about the junk food I planned to eat. I wasn't going to completely pig out, but I planned to enjoy some unhealthy food.*

The break was a bad decision. I experienced unwanted consequences. I felt lousy for four days after the break. I had no energy, could hardly get out of bed, and felt sluggish. My attitude was unstable and flashed like a strobe light, rapidly switching from happy to sad, cheerful to mad, lively to depressed, and nice to mean for no apparent reason. I had to fight incredible sugar cravings and felt nauseated, foggy headed, and just plain bad!

I didn't think a weekend break would be a big deal. I thought I could pick up on Monday morning right where I left off. Wrong! Without realizing it, my break left an opening for the enemy. I did everything I could think of to feel better, but nothing seemed to work. By Thursday, I was at my wits' end. I turned to spiritual warfare. I anointed myself with oil, prayed, and proclaimed the Word of God over myself. The same day I got better. Thank God!

I pray I'll never forget the terrible price I paid for a break that turned out not to be a break at all. I never again want that type of "liberty," because it really wasn't freedom. Instead, I was ruled by my flesh and the ill effects of poor eating. The result was sinfulness instead of righteous living.

"Let the one who is righteous continue to live righteously; let the one who is holy continue to be holy. Look, I am coming soon, bringing my reward with me to repay all people according to their deeds."

—Revelation 22:11–12 NLT

NO BREAKS IN WAR

I was foolish to think I could take a break from living righteously. How stupid of me! In the first place, to take a break means to stop doing something. The second I took a break from eating healthfully and honoring my temple, I immediately stopped living righteously.

When it comes to holy living, there's no such thing as a break. You are either living in a holy manner or you aren't. It stands to reason that if you break from righteous living, unrighteous living will occur—and that's exactly what happened!

Like it or not, we are in a perpetual war. Our adversary, the devil, knows his time is short. Because of this, he never breaks from seeking ways to destroy us and to get us to sin. He is always lurking! Since he is always waging war, we must always be ready to fight and defend. We cannot break from guarding or honoring our temples. Taking a break is what the enemy wants us to do.

Taking a break near a vicious enemy who never takes breaks will get you seriously wounded or killed. In wartime, soldiers are always on alert. They don't even take full-blown breaks in the restroom. Even then, they're on high alert and ready to fight. Those fully invested in war sleep "with one eye open." There are no breaks in war!

GOD REWARDS US

On another note, "rewarding" yourself with things that aren't good for you is a trick of the enemy. Think about it. How can you reward yourself with something harmful? There is nothing good in anything harmful.

More than that, I don't recall reading about rewarding yourself in the Bible. As stated in Revelation 22:12, God will reward us. If we let Him reward us, the reward will be well deserved and appropriate. The rewards we attempt to give ourselves can only come from selfish, self-centered places and aren't necessarily appropriate or deserved. Instead of rewarding ourselves, our focus should be on honoring God and living in a way that brings Him glory.

Here is the kicker: not only will God reward us in this life, but He will also dispense eternal rewards. God keeps a record of everything we do, and on judgment day He will reward us according to our deeds (Rev. 2:23; 20:12). For this reason, we must be mindful of what we do. It's sobering to think the things we do now determine how we'll spend eternity. I know how much I like it when God rewards me for obeying Him. I definitely don't want to miss out on any eternal rewards because I live disobediently now.

It's important to realize all of our actions have consequences—some pleasant, others unpleasant. Some consequences will be meted out now, others during eternity. These consequences will come either as blessings or curses. They will affect every area of your life—your living, travels, ideas, posterity, finances, possessions, environment, you name it. They will even affect your health. I want to receive blessings. I want you to have the same, which is why I'm sharing this with you.

Blessings for Obedience

Leviticus 26 and Deuteronomy 28 tell about God's blessings and curses for Israel, His chosen people. Even though the specifics of these verses are directed toward Israel, the principles of blessings for obedience and curses for disobedience still apply today. We'll first look at the blessings for obedience in Deuteronomy 28:1–13. These are my summaries of how these verses relate to us today, but the depths of God's blessings are much greater than anything I can fathom.

- If you fully obey the LORD God in every area of your life, He will raise you to an exalted place in Him (v. 1).
- Every blessing in His Word will chase you down, overtake you, and remain with you if you obey Him (v. 2).
- You will be blessed everywhere you go (v. 3).
- Everything birthed in you—your offspring, dreams, visions, ideas, and so forth—as well as your land and possessions, will be blessed (v. 4).
- Your food storage and food preparation will be blessed (v. 5).

- You will be blessed wherever you go (v. 6).
- The Lord will defeat your enemies before you and will cause them to scatter (v. 7).
- The Lord will send a blessing on everything you do. He will even bless your savings and storage places (v. 8).
- The Lord will raise you to be holy (v. 9).
- People will recognize you as one of God's children, and they will be in awe of you (v. 10).
- The Lord will grant you abundant prosperity. Your children, dreams, visions, ideas, and property will prosper. The seeds you sow will be blessed (v. 11).
- The Lord will send an overabundance of heavenly blessings on everything you do. These blessings will enable you to give to nations of people without having to borrow or use credit (v. 12).
- The Lord will put you on top and never on the bottom; always move you upward and never downward (v. 13).

Curses for Disobedience

In Deuteronomy 28, there are four times the number of scriptures on curses than there are on blessings. I am guessing God wants us to understand He is serious about punishing disobedience. He is a loving God, but He is also just.

For the sake of space, I won't list every curse, but I pray you will still get the gist of the distressing things that can happen if we disobey God. The curses for disobedience are based on Deuteronomy 28:15–68 (NLT). As mentioned earlier, the specific curses were directed toward Israel, but the principles are still applicable today. Again, I have summarized them to make them relatable now.

- You will receive opposite the blessings for obedience (vv. 16–19).
- The Lord will send curses, confusion, and frustration in everything you do (v. 20).
- The Lord will strike you with wasting diseases, fever, inflammation, drought, and blight (v. 22).
- The Lord will afflict you with boils, tumors, scurvy (bleeding gums and spots on the skin), and an itch, which cannot be cured (v. 27).

- The Lord will strike you with madness, blindness, and panic (v. 28).
- You will be engaged to a woman (or man), but another man (or woman) will sleep with her (or him). You will build a house, but someone else will live in it. You will plant crops, but you will never enjoy any of them (v. 30).
- You will go mad because of all the tragedy you see around you (v. 34).
- You will become an object of horror, ridicule, and mockery (v. 37).

Please don't fool yourself into thinking these things can't happen to you. God will hold you accountable for the things of which you have knowledge. And don't think it won't happen to you because you know of others who disobey God and seem to get away with it. I warn you, don't take the chance!

God doesn't want to punish us, but He understands the destructive consequences of sin. He repeatedly warns us of sin's consequences, and He lovingly tells us what to do to receive His blessings instead. Because God is holy and just, He must deal with sin harshly; because He is loving and merciful, He provides a way to escape His wrath.

The way to escape God's wrath is to accept Christ's death as atonement for our sins. If we accept Christ as the payment for our sins, we receive forgiveness, blessings, and eternal paradise with God (Luke 23:39–43). If we don't, we pay the price for our sins, suffer curses, and receive eternal punishment without God (Rom. 2:5–8).

Even if we receive God's forgiveness, we still have to deal with the consequences of our actions during our lifetime (Heb. 12:5–6; 2 Sam. 11–12:24).

YOU REAP WHAT YOU SOW

No one gets away with sin or disobedience. There is a return for everything you do. You'll either get a positive or negative return. This is a biblical principle called the law of sowing and reaping. This law is found in many places in the Bible, but we're going to look at four passages.

As long as the earth remains, there will be *planting and harvest* (emphasis mine), cold and heat, summer and winter, day and night.
—Genesis 8:22 NLT

The wicked man earns deceitful wages, but he who sows righteousness (moral and spiritual rectitude in every area and relation) shall have a sure reward [permanent and satisfying].
—Proverbs 11:18 AMP

Remember this: Whoever sows sparingly will also reap sparingly, and whoever sows generously will also reap generously.
—2 Corinthians 9:6 NIV

Do not be deceived: God cannot be mocked. A man reaps what he sows. Whoever sows to please their flesh, from the flesh will reap destruction; whoever sows to please the Spirit, from the Spirit will reap eternal life. Let us not become weary in doing good, for at the proper time we will reap a harvest if we do not give up.
—Galatians 6:7–9 NIV

The law of sowing and reaping says that whatever you sow (put out) is what you will reap (get back). If you sow something good, you will get something good back. For instance, if you are stingy, don't expect others to give to you. This law also says you will get back the amount you sow. If you give a lot, you'll get a lot in return.

Galatians 6:7 says, "Do not be deceived." This is telling us not to be fooled or misled by delays or what we see happening around us. Our harvest is a matter of time. The good (or bad) we disseminate will come back to us! There is no mocking God. He keeps His word. Recall what God said in Deuteronomy 28: there will be blessings if we obey Him and curses if we don't.

Galatians 6:9 says, "Let us not become weary." This verse tells us it will take time for our seeds to produce a harvest (result). Don't doubt, stop believing in, or get tired of waiting for your harvest (reward). It will come in time.

There is much more to say about sowing and reaping, but my goal here is for you to understand that your every deed has a resulting consequence. You will get back whatever you put out.

You will even reap what you sow into your health.

- You eat unhealthy things, and you reap unhealthiness.
- You eat fattening foods, and you reap fatness.
- You eat high-cholesterol foods, and you reap high cholesterol in your bloodstream.
- You don't get enough rest, and you reap less energy.
- You put good things into your mind, and you'll reap good thoughts and be more optimistic.
- You stop worrying, and you reap less stress.

The same is true in your relationships.

- You don't invest in building relationships, and they will fall apart.
- You don't help or give to others, and others won't help or give to you.
- You don't encourage or lift others, and others won't encourage or lift you.
- You are mean and crabby, and others will be mean and crabby to you.

The bottom line? You reap what you sow

- in *thoughts* (what you think about will happen, so think good thoughts),
- in *words* (what you say will come to pass, so say right things), and
- in *deeds* (what you do will come back to you, so do what brings blessings).

Please understand, this does not mean that everything that happens to you (be it good or bad) is because you sowed it. It does mean, however, that *something* will happen as a result of what you sow. For example, in John 9:2–3, Jesus' disciples wanted to know if the man was born blind because of his sin or his parents' sin. Basically, Jesus said no one was to blame, but he was born blind so God's power could be displayed through his healing. His blindness didn't happen because he sowed it. It happened because God willed it so He could get glory from it. Sometimes bad (or good) things happen to people because God wills it, not because anything was done to warrant it.

Some people suffer with disease without having done anything to deserve it. Some people are born with abnormalities that have nothing to do with what they've sown. Yet others suffer with illnesses because of what they've sown. If you are someone who maintains an unhealthy diet and poor lifestyle habits, you place yourself at risk for developing high blood pressure, heart disease, type 2 diabetes, and certain cancers.[1]

OWN IT

I hate to admit it, but I'm still overweight even though I've lost a considerable amount of weight. I'm overweight as a result of my actions. To put it another way, I've reaped what I've sown. My eating isn't as healthy as it should be; therefore, my weight isn't what it should be.

I eat too much fat. I eat lots of olive oil and coconut oil, which are good fats, but fats nonetheless. I eat too close to bedtime. (When we sleep, our bodies are less active and use less energy, or calories. It's best to stop eating two to three hours before going to bed.) I still struggle with eating past the point of being satisfied to the point where I'm almost full. (Our bodies store the calories they don't need as fat.) Even though I've had some hormonal imbalances and thyroid issues that have made losing weight somewhat of a challenge, I can't blame being overweight on anything other than myself. The root of my problem lies in how I eat. Once I get my eating under control, my weight will be under control. The amount I weigh depends on me.

The good news is I use my body to exercise, walk, line dance, take Zumba classes, and play sports. I sowed into moving my body; therefore, I reaped the ability to move. The more I do with my body, the more capable I'm finding my body to be. How fit my body is depends on me.

I used to blame my weight on many other things. I've said things like "I have a slow metabolism," "People in my family have weight issues, so I probably will too," "Something in my body isn't working properly and is keeping me from getting weight off," and "I don't eat a lot." (When I tracked my food intake, I found out I was eating more than I thought. Those small snacks all day added up.)

It can be painful to look at yourself and admit truths that show your sinfulness. While writing this book, I cried many times facing the shameful things I've done. But when I get down on myself, God reminds me I'm a work in progress, and I'm getting there. I haven't reached the point of optimal health or the best weight for me, but I've made considerable progress, and I haven't turned back! The process has been slow but steady.

What about you? Are you experiencing consequences for something you know you didn't sow, like the man born blind? If so, don't be sad or depressed, but seek ways to give God glory. If you, like me, are reaping the consequences of what you've sown, I encourage you to do something about it.

Friend, I say to you, look at your life. Is it the way you want it to be? Is your health where it could be? Are you at a good weight for you? If the answer to any of these questions is no, you have the power to change things. Own it. Make no more excuses. Choose to live in a way that is holy, acceptable, and pleasing to God. It's within your power to *Worship God! And Praise Away the Pounds!*

Call to Action

1. Think of a time you took a break (or stopped doing something) when you shouldn't have and something unwanted happened. What could have made things turn out better?
2. What are you doing now that if you stopped doing it would make your life better?
3. What is something positive you've reaped from what you've sown? What is something negative?
4. What are some things you need to stop making excuses for and own?
5. What action is God prompting you to take?

Thank You, Father, for equipping me with power. You've given me power to withstand and overcome every single ploy of the enemy. I have power to resist temptation; You always give me ways of escape. I have power to overcome sickness and disease; by Your stripes I am healed and made whole. You've given me the power of the Holy Spirit within me as my weapon of victory.

No power in heaven or on earth can withstand You, and You live within me. I am more than a conqueror through You. I have the Father, Son, and Holy Spirit on my side; therefore, nothing can prevail over me. Help me to remember I can do anything through You because You give me strength. I thank You in advance for the perfect blessings in store for me. Help me to give You the utmost praise in everything I do. In Jesus' name I pray. Amen.

FINAL THOUGHTS

Y OUR JOURNEY DOESN'T end just because you've finished this book. Your journey will never end—not until you reach heaven. Then you'll be on a different kind of journey:

A journey filled with experiencing greater blessings than you can ever imagine!

A journey filled with rewards based on the choices you make in life.

A journey that's pure joy, where there is no more sin or pain.

So keep pressing toward the mark for the prize of your high calling. You will make mistakes and get off track, but don't worry or get bent out of shape. God doesn't expect us to be perfect. He understands our shortcomings, which is why He shows us so much mercy. Strive for perfection—holiness and maturity. That way, you'll be closer to it when you reach heaven!

Read the Word. Study it. Meditate on its precepts. Apply it to your life. Read other Christian materials that will help you stay on track. (You can even read this book again!)

The enemy has sent many things—not just food—to weigh us down. His weights come in the form of addictions, problems, and sin. Whatever you do, resist them. Fight hard! Even if you repeatedly find yourself falling for his schemes, refocus and get back on track. Just don't quit! The battle isn't over until you're dead. As long as you have breath in your body, live—no, fight—to *Worship God! And Praise Away the Pounds!*

May you recognize and use the power God has given you.

—Tonya

APPENDIX

T HE FOLLOWING PAGES can be used a variety of ways. When I created them, I wanted to track the details of my life to see whether or not the way I spent my days reflected my priorities. I also wanted to develop a way to help me focus on things I considered important.

For starters, I made enough copies of "Today's Focus" and "How I Spent My Day" to track for two months. I made only enough copies of the "How Much Time I Spent in Each Category" and "Journal" pages to use at the end of each week of the two months. I bound everything together into a booklet for easy use.

Before beginning, I listed my priorities in order of importance under "How Much Time I Spent in Each Category." (I suggest no more than ten and no fewer than five.) My categories were *Spiritual, Self-Care, Family, Career, Social Relationships,* and *Miscellaneous.* (Yours may be different from mine.) Each day, before getting out of bed, I completed the things on the "Today's Focus" page through "I must surrender (yield to, let go of)." Each night, I completed the remainder of the page, beginning with "Today I am grateful for." As the day progressed, I noted how I spent my time. I noted everything, including things like praying, getting dressed, eating, watching TV, phone/computer time, sleeping, driving, etc. At the end of each day, I added up the amount of time spent in each category and recorded it. At the end of each week, I calculated the total time spent in each category. I did this for two months. I learned a lot!

On various occasions, I copied and used only "Today's Focus" to help me gain spiritual focus when I felt myself drifting from the things of God. I've also used it when I needed to focus on specific areas for spiritual growth. On a few occasions, I copied and used "How I Spent My Day" when I felt my priorities were getting out of order.

Here are some of the things I learned using these pages:

- Whether the way I spent my time reflected my true priorities
- The amount of time I wasted on unimportant things
- The amount of time I spent on things of God
- The amount of time I spent eating, sleeping, with my family, at work, doing leisure activities, etc.
- How to get the most out of each day
- How to stay focused on God's priorities
- How to be less self-centered and more God centered
- How to be more grateful
- How well I did regarding health and fitness

Feel free to copy the parts you need to help you live with intention.

Today's Focus

Date: _____

Today's Focus: _____

    Specific actions to help accomplish today's focus:

_____

_____

During my time with God, He revealed, asked, commanded:

_____

Scripture reference/support:

_____

Today's priorities:

_____

I must surrender (yield to, let go of):

_____

Today, I am grateful for:

_____

_____

Today, I pleased and/or obeyed God by:

_____

_____

Awarenesses/Revelations:

How I Spent My Day

6:00 AM		2:00 PM		10:00 PM	
6:30 AM		2:30 PM		10:30 PM	
7:00 AM		3:00 PM		11:00 PM	
7:30 AM		3:30 PM		11:30 PM	
8:00 AM		4:00 PM		12 MID	
8:30 AM		4:30 PM		12:30 AM	
9:00 AM		5:00 PM		1:00 AM	
9:30 AM		5:30 PM		1:30 AM	
10:00AM		6:00 PM		2:00 AM	
10:30AM		6:30 PM		2:30 AM	
11:00AM		7:00 PM		3:00 AM	
11:30AM		7:30 PM		3:30 AM	
12 NOON		8:00 PM		4:00 AM	
12:30PM		8:30 PM		4:30 AM	
1:00 PM		9:00 PM		5:00 AM	
1:30 PM		9:30 PM		5:30 AM	

Health & Fitness			
Exercise: N___ Y___ How Long?_____ Water: # of cups _____			
Breakfast	Lunch	Dinner	Snack

How Much Time I Spent in Each Category

Week of _____

(Write your priorities in order from most important to least, then calculate the amount of time you spent in each category.)

Categories	Mon	Tue	Wed	Thu	Fri	Sat	Sun	Week Total

Awarenesses/Revelations: .

Journal

*What needs to change? What doesn't? What went well? What didn't?
Any insights?*

HELPFUL SCRIPTURES

HERE YOU'LL FIND some of the Scriptures that have helped me on my Romans 12:1–2 journey. I encourage you to personalize them and then pray them to the Lord, who desires to heal you. His Word will accomplish everything He sent it to accomplish (Isa. 55:11). Believe it!

Losing Weight God's Way

Therefore I always exercise and discipline myself [mortifying my body, deadening my carnal affections, bodily appetites, and worldly desires, endeavoring in all respects] to have a clear (unshaken, blameless) conscience, void of offense toward God and toward men (Acts 24:16 AMP).

> Don't you know that you yourselves are God's temple and that God's Spirit lives in you? If anyone destroys God's temple, God will destroy him; for God's temple is sacred, and you are that temple.
> —1 Corinthians 3:16–17 NIV

> Everything is permissible (allowable and lawful) for me; but not all things are helpful (good for me to do, expedient and profitable when considered with other things). Everything is lawful for me, but I will not become the slave of anything or be brought under its power.
> —1 Corinthians 6:12 AMP

> You know the old saying, "First you eat to live, and then you live to eat"? Well, it may be true that the body is only a temporary thing,

but that's no excuse for stuffing your body with food, or indulging it with sex. Since the Master honors you with a body, honor him with your body!

—1 Corinthians 6:13 MSG

Do you not know that your body is a temple of the Holy Spirit, who is in you, whom you have received from God? You are not your own.

—1 Corinthians 6:19 NIV

Don't you realize that your body is the temple of the Holy Spirit, who lives in you and was given to you by God? You do not belong to yourself.

—1 Corinthians 6:19 NLT

I discipline my body like an athlete, training it to do what it should.

—1 Corinthians 9:27 NLT

No temptation has seized you except what is common to man. And God is faithful; he will not let you be tempted beyond what you can bear. But when you are tempted, he will also provide a way out so that you can stand up under it.

—1 Corinthians 10:13 NIV

So whether you eat or drink, or whatever you do, do it all for the glory of God.

—1 Corinthians 10:31 NLT

So, come out from among [unbelievers], and separate (sever) yourselves from them, says the Lord, and touch not [any] unclean thing; then I will receive you kindly and treat you with favor.

—2 Corinthians 6:17 AMP

For though we live in the world, we do not wage war as the world does. The weapons we fight with are not the weapons of the world. On the contrary, they have divine power to demolish strongholds. We demolish arguments and every pretension that sets itself up against the knowledge of God, and we take captive every thought to make it obedient to Christ.

—2 Corinthians 10:3–5 NIV

Two people are better off than one, for they can help each other succeed.

—Ecclesiastes 4:9 NLT

For our struggle is not against flesh and blood, but against the rulers, against the authorities, against the powers of this dark world and against the spiritual forces of evil in the heavenly realms.

—Ephesians 6:12 NIV

But I say, walk and live [habitually] in the [Holy] Spirit [responsive to and controlled and guided by the Spirit]; then you will certainly not gratify the cravings and desires of the flesh (of human nature without God).

—Galatians 5:16 AMP

Therefore, since we are surrounded by such a great cloud of witnesses, let us throw off everything that hinders and the sin that so easily entangles. And let us run with perseverance the race marked out for us.

—Hebrews 12:1 NIV

Do you see what this means—all these pioneers who blazed the way, all these veterans cheering us on? It means we'd better get on with it. Strip down, start running—and never quit! No extra spiritual fat, no parasitic sins. Keep your eyes on Jesus, who both began and finished this race we're in. Study how he did it. Because he never lost sight of where he was headed—that exhilarating finish in and with God—he could put up with anything along the way: Cross, shame, whatever. And now he's there, in the place of honor, right alongside God. When you find yourselves flagging in your faith, go over that story again, item by item, that long litany of hostility he plowed through. That will shoot adrenaline into your souls!

—Hebrews 12:1–3 MSG

No discipline seems pleasant at the time, but painful. Later on, however, it produces a harvest of righteousness and peace for those who have been trained by it.

—Hebrews 12:11 NIV

So don't sit around on your hands! No more dragging your feet! Clear the path for long-distance runners so no one will trip and fall, so no one will step in a hole and sprain an ankle. Help each other out. And run for it!

—Hebrews 12:12–13 MSG

So Jesus said to those Jews who had believed in Him, If you abide in My word [hold fast to My teachings and live in accordance with them], you are truly My disciples. And you will know the Truth, and the Truth will set you free.

—John 8:31–32 AMP

The thief's purpose is to steal and kill and destroy. My purpose is to give them a rich and satisfying life.

—John 10:10 NLT

And now, children, stay with Christ. Live deeply in Christ. Then we'll be ready for him when he appears, ready to receive him with open arms, with no cause for red-faced guilt or lame excuses when he arrives.

—1 John 2:28 MSG

And now, dear children, continue in him, so that when he appears we may be confident and unashamed before him at his coming.

—1 John 2:28 NIV

Then Jesus said to His disciples, If anyone desires to be My disciple, let him deny himself [disregard, lose sight of, and forget himself and his own interests] and take up his cross and follow Me cleave steadfastly to Me, conform wholly to My example in living and, if need be, in dying, also]. For whoever is bent on saving his [temporal] life [his comfort and security here] shall lose it [eternal life]; and whoever loses his life [his comfort and security here] for My sake shall find it [life everlasting].

—Matthew 16:24–25 AMP

Then Jesus went to work on his disciples. "Anyone who intends to come with me has to let me lead. You're not in the driver's seat; I am. Don't run from suffering; embrace it. Follow me and I'll show you how. Self-help is no help at all. Self-sacrifice is the way, my way, to finding yourself, your true self. What kind of deal is it to get everything you want but lose yourself? What could you ever trade your soul for?

—Matthew 16:24–26 MSG

Then Jesus said to his disciples, "If any of you wants to be my follower, you must turn from your selfish ways, take up your cross, and follow me. If you try to hang on to your life, you will lose it. But if you give up your life for my sake, you will save it."

—Matthew 16:24–25 NLT

All of you must keep awake (give strict attention, be cautious and active) and watch and pray, that you may not come into temptation. The spirit indeed is willing, but the flesh is weak.

—Matthew 26:41 AMP

Keep watch and pray, so that you will not give in to temptation. For the spirit is willing, but the body is weak!

—Matthew 26:41 NLT

This is in keeping with my own eager desire and persistent expectation and hope, that I shall not disgrace myself nor be put to shame in anything; but that with the utmost freedom of speech and unfailing courage, now as always heretofore, Christ (the Messiah) will be magnified and get glory and praise in this body of mine and be boldly exalted in my person, whether through (by) life or through (by) death. For me to live is Christ [His life in me], and to die is gain [the gain of the glory of eternity].

—Philippians 1:20–21 AMP

Brothers, I do not consider myself yet to have taken hold of it. But one thing I do: Forgetting what is behind and straining toward what is ahead, I press on toward the goal to win the prize for which God has called me heavenward in Christ Jesus.

—Philippians 3:13–14 NIV

I have strength for all things in Christ Who empowers me [I am ready for anything and equal to anything through Him Who infuses inner strength into me; I am self-sufficient in Christ's sufficiency].

—Philippians 4:13 AMP

Trust in the LORD with all your heart and lean not on your own understanding; in all your ways acknowledge him, and he will make your paths straight.

—Proverbs 3:5–6 NIV

The LORD is my Shepherd [to feed, guide, and shield me], I shall not lack.

—Psalm 23:1 AMP

We are assured and know that [God being a partner in their labor] all things work together and are [fitting into a plan] for good to and for those who love God and are called according to [His] design and purpose.

—Romans 8:28 AMP

Therefore, I urge you, brothers, in view of God's mercy, to offer your bodies as living sacrifices, holy and pleasing to God—this is your spiritual act of worship. Do not conform any longer to the pattern of this world, but be transformed by the renewing of your mind. Then you will be able to test and approve what God's will is—his good, pleasing and perfect will.

—Romans 12:1–2 NIV

That each one of you should know how to possess (control, manage) his own body in consecration (purity, separated from things profane) and honor.

—1 Thessalonians 4:4 AMP

Blessed Health

He said, "If you listen carefully to the LORD your God and do what is right in his eyes, if you pay attention to his commands and keep all his decrees, I will not bring on you any of the diseases I brought on the Egyptians, for I am the LORD, who heals you" (Exod. 15:26 NIV).

"Worship the LORD your God, and his blessing will be on your food and water. I will take away sickness from among you, and none will miscarry or be barren in your land. I will give you a full life span."

—Exodus 23:25–26 NIV

But He was wounded for our transgressions, He was bruised for our guilt and iniquities; the chastisement [needful to obtain] peace and well-being for us was upon Him, and with the stripes [that wounded] Him we are healed and made whole.

—Isaiah 53:5 AMP

Is anyone among you sick? Let them call the elders of the church to pray over them and anoint them with oil in the name of the Lord. And the prayer offered in faith will make the sick person well; the Lord will raise them up. If they have sinned, they will be forgiven. Therefore confess your sins to each other and pray for each other so that you may be healed. The prayer of a righteous person is powerful and effective.

—James 5:14–16 NIV

And the prayer offered in faith will make the sick person well; the Lord will raise them up. If they have sinned, they will be forgiven.

—James 5:15 NIV

Heal me, Lord, and I will be healed; save me and I will be saved, for you are the one I praise.

—Jeremiah 17:14 NIV

"But I will restore you to health and heal your wounds," declares the LORD.

—Jeremiah 30:17 NIV

Dear friend, I pray that you may enjoy good health and that all may go well with you, even as your soul is getting along well.

—3 John 1:2 NIV

"Daughter, your faith has healed you. Go in peace and be freed from your suffering."

—Mark 5:34 NIV

Then He touched their eyes, saying, According to your faith and trust and reliance [on the power invested in Me] be it done to you.

—Matthew 9:29 AMP

Then he touched their eyes and said, "According to your faith will it be done to you."

—Matthew 9:29 NIV

"He himself bore our sins" in his body on the cross, so that we might die to sins and live for righteousness; "by his wounds you have been healed."

—1 Peter 2:24 NIV

Be well balanced (temperate, sober of mind), be vigilant and cautious at all times; for that enemy of yours, the devil, roams around like a lion roaring [in fierce hunger], seeking someone to seize upon and devour.

—1 Peter 5:8 AMP

Do not be wise in your own eyes; fear the LORD and shun evil. This will bring health to your body and nourishment to your bones.

—Proverbs 3:7–8 NIV

My child, listen to me and do as I say, and you will have a long, good life.

—Proverbs 4:10 NLT

My son, pay attention to what I say; turn your ear to my words. Do not let them out of your sight, keep them within your heart; for they are life to those who find them and health to one's whole body.

—Proverbs 4:20–22 NIV

He brought me forth also into a large place; he delivered me, because he delighted in me.

—Psalm 18:19 KJV

LORD my God, I called to you for help, and you healed me.

—Psalm 30:2 NIV

GOD, my God, I yelled for help and you put me together. GOD, you pulled me out of the grave, gave me another chance at life when I was down-and-out.

—Psalm 30:2–3 MSG

Praise the LORD, my soul, and forget not all his benefits—who forgives all your sins and heals all your diseases, who redeems your life from the pit and crowns you with love and compassion, who satisfies your desires with good things so that your youth is renewed like the eagle's.
—Psalm 103:2–5 NIV

Some of you were sick because you'd lived a bad life, your bodies feeling the effects of your sin; You couldn't stand the sight of food, so miserable you thought you'd be better off dead. Then you called out to GOD in your desperate condition; he got you out in the nick of time. He spoke the word that healed you, that pulled you back from the brink of death. So thank GOD for his marvelous love, for his miracle mercy to the children he loves; Offer thanksgiving sacrifices, tell the world what he's done—sing it out!
—Psalm 107:17–22 MSG

He sent out his word and healed them; he rescued them from the grave.
—Psalm 107:20 NIV

I will not die; instead, I will live to tell what the LORD has done.
—Psalm 118:17 NLT

May God himself, the God who makes everything holy and whole, make you holy and whole, put you together—spirit, soul, and body—and keep you fit for the coming of our Master, Jesus Christ. The One who called you is completely dependable. If he said it, he'll do it!
—1 Thessalonians 5:23–24 MSG

A Blessed Mind

"Therefore if any person is [ingrafted] in Christ (the Messiah) he is a new creation (a new creature altogether); the old [previous moral and spiritual condition] has passed away. Behold, the fresh and new has come!" (2 Cor. 5:17 AMP).

For though we walk (live) in the flesh, we are not carrying on our warfare according to the flesh and using mere human weapons. For the weapons of our warfare are not physical [weapons of flesh and blood], but they are mighty before God for the overthrow and destruction of strongholds,

191

[Inasmuch as we] refute arguments and theories and reasonings and every proud and lofty thing that sets itself up against the [true] knowledge of God; and we lead every thought and purpose away captive into the obedience of Christ (the Messiah, the Anointed One).

—2 Corinthians 10:3–5 AMP

Be strong in the Lord [be empowered through your union with Him]; draw your strength from Him [that strength which His boundless might provides].

—Ephesians 6:10 AMP

The Lord God is my Strength, my personal bravery, and my invincible army; He makes my feet like hinds' feet and will make me to walk [not to stand still in terror, but to walk] and make [spiritual] progress upon my high places [of trouble, suffering, or responsibility]!

—Habakkuk 3:19 AMP

You will guard him and keep him in perfect and constant peace whose mind [both its inclination and its character] is stayed on You, because he commits himself to You, leans on You, and hopes confidently in You.

—Isaiah 26:3 AMP

Then shall your light break forth like the morning, and your healing (your restoration and the power of a new life) shall spring forth speedily; your righteousness (your rightness, your justice, and your right relationship with God) shall go before you [conducting you to peace and prosperity], and the glory of the Lord shall be your rear guard.

—Isaiah 58:8 AMP

The earnest (heartfelt, continued) prayer of a righteous man makes tremendous power available [dynamic in its working].

—James 5:16 AMP

The thief comes only in order to steal and kill and destroy. I came that they may have and enjoy life, and have it in abundance (to the full, till it overflows).

—John 10:10 AMP

[Yes] I will grant [I Myself will do for you] whatever you shall ask in My Name [as presenting all that I Am].

—John 14:14 AMP

You may ask me for anything in my name, and I will do it.

—John 14:14 NIV

I am the vine; you are the branches. If a man remains in me and I in him, he will bear much fruit; apart from me you can do nothing.

—John 15:5 NIV

Have I not commanded you? Be strong and courageous. Do not be terrified; do not be discouraged, for the LORD your God will be with you wherever you go.

—Joshua 1:9 NIV

Therefore I tell you, whatever you ask for in prayer, believe that you have received it, and it will be yours.

—Mark 11:24 NIV

Then He touched their eyes, saying, "According to your faith and trust and reliance [on the power invested in Me] be it done to you."

—Matthew 9:29 AMP

Then he touched their eyes and said, "According to your faith will it be done to you."

—Matthew 9:29 NIV

Keep a cool head. Stay alert. The Devil is poised to pounce, and would like nothing better than to catch you napping. Keep your guard up.

—1 Peter 5:8 MSG

Lean on, trust in, and be confident in the Lord with all your heart and mind and do not rely on your own insight or understanding. In all your ways know, recognize, and acknowledge Him, and He will direct and make straight and plain your paths.

—Proverbs 3:5–6 AMP

Pleasant words are as a honeycomb, sweet to the mind and healing to the body.

—Proverbs 16:24 AMP

A happy heart is good medicine and a cheerful mind works healing, but a broken spirit dries up the bones.

—Proverbs 17:22 AMP

He led me to a place of safety; he rescued me because he delights in me.

—Psalm 18:19 NLT

The LORD is my shepherd; I have all that I need.

—Psalm 23:1 NLT

He heals the brokenhearted and binds up their wounds [curing their pains and their sorrows].

—Psalm 147:3 AMP

For God did not give us a spirit of timidity (of cowardice, of craven and cringing and fawning fear), but [He has given us a spirit] of power and of love and of calm and well-balanced mind and discipline and self-control.

—2 Timothy 1:7 AMP

NOTES

Chapter 1: Change

1. Robert Jamieson, A. R. Fausset, and David Brown, *Commentary on the Whole Bible* (Grand Rapids, MI: Zondervan, 1961), 1174.
2. *Riverside Webster's II Dictionary.*
3. *The Student Bible Dictionary.*
4. *Noah Webster 1828 American Dictionary of the English Language,* facsimile ed.
5. *Riverside Webster's II Dictionary.*
6. *Noah Webster 1828 American Dictionary of the English Language,* facsimile ed.
7. http://everything2.com/title/surrender.

Chapter 2: Put God First

1. http://bible.org/article/biblical-meditation.

Chapter 3: Steps to Stay on Track

1. http://en.wikipedia.org/wiki/Accountability.
2. http://wiki.answers.com/Q/What_does_governance_mean.

Chapter 5: Get Moving

1. Jordan Rubin and Nicki Rubin, *The Great Physician's RX for Women's Health* (Nashville, TN: Thomas Nelson, 2006), 132–133.
2. Scott Conard, *Weight Loss the Jabez Way* (Southlake, TX: Inprov, Ltd., 2009), 66.
3. *Webster's New World Thesaurus.*

Chapter 6: Set Apart for God

1. *Noah Webster 1828 American Dictionary of the English Language,* facsimile ed.
2. *Student Bible Dictionary.*
3. Jamieson, Fausset, and Brown, 1174.

Chapter 9: Well-Pleasing Service

1. Jamieson, Fausset, and Brown, 1174.

Chapter 12: Dress Differently

1. W. E. Vine, Merrill F. Unger, William White, Jr., *Vine's Complete Expository Dictionary of Old and New Testament Words* (Nashville, TN: Thomas Nelson, 1996), New Testament section 122.
2. James Strong, *The New Strong's Expanded Exhaustive Concordance of the Bible Red Letter Edition* (Nashville, TN: Thomas Nelson, 2001); G4964, 244.

Chapter 13: Find True Freedom

1. http://www.audioenglish.net/dictionary/bondage.htm.
2. Ibid.
3. Dictionary search "bondage," http://www.google.com.
4. Ibid.
5. http://www.definitions.net/definition/bondage.
6. Ibid.
7. *New American Webster's College Dictionary.*
8. Dictionary search "freedom," http://www.google.com.
9. Ibid.

10. http://www.merriam-webster.com/dictionary/freedom?show=0&t=1305318278.
11. Ibid.
12. http://dictionary.reference.com/browse/freedom.
13. Ibid.

Chapter 14: From Caterpillar to Butterfly

1. http://www.blueletterbible.org/lang/lexicon/lexicon.cfm?Strongs=G3339&t=KJV.
2. *Riverside Webster's II Dictionary.*
3. *The New American Webster's Handy College Dictionary.*
4. *Random House Webster's Dictionary.*
5. http://www.earthlife.net/insects/lepidop1.html.

Chapter 15: Livin' and Walkin'

1. http://en.wikipedia.org/wiki/Digital_television_transition_in_the_United_States.
2. http://en.wikipedia.org/wiki/Low_power_television.
3. http://en.wikipedia.org/wiki/Digital_television_transition_in_the_United_States.
4. *Collins English Dictionary – Complete and Unabridged.*
5. http://www.mayoclinic.com/health/walking/HQ01612.
6. http://weight-loss.emedtv.com/exercise/benefits-of-walking.html.
7. http://www.cambridgema.gov/CDD/Transportation/gettingaround-cambridge/byfoot/healthbenefits.aspx.

Chapter 16: Heart Matters

1. http://www.blueletterbible.org/lang/lexicon/lexicon.cfm?Strongs=H3820&t=KJV.
2. http://www.blueletterbible.org/lang/lexicon/lexicon.cfm?Strongs=H3559&t=KJV.
3. http://www.blueletterbible.org/lang/lexicon/lexicon.cfm?Strongs=H7307&t=KJV.
4. John Eldredge, *Waking the Dead* (Nashville, TN: Thomas Nelson, 2003), 98.

5. http://www.blueletterbible.org/lang/lexicon/lexicon.cfm?Strongs=
   G342&t=KJV.
6. Jamieson, Fausset, and Brown, 1174.

Chapter 18: What's Eating You?

1. http://www.hsph.harvard.edu/nutritionsource/what-should-you-eat/
   fiber-full-story/index.html.
2. K-State Research and Extension *Master Food Volunteer Handbook*,
   chapter 6—Preparing Fruits and Vegetables, 4.
3. Family Nutrition Education Programs *Steps to a Healthier You*,
   lesson 4—Make Mine Low-fat Milk, 4.
4. http://www.hsph.harvard.edu/nutritionsource/what-should-you-eat/
   protein-full-story/index.html.
5. http://www.cdc.gov/healthyweight/calories/index.html.

Chapter 19: Establish Yourself

1. Jamieson, Fausset, and Brown, 1449.
2. Finis Jennings Dake, *Dake's Annotated Reference Bible, King James
   Version* (Lawrenceville, GA: Dake Bible Sales, Inc., 1991), NT, b.
   (Romans 12:2), 170.
3. Hebrews 5:12–14 note, *Life Application Study Bible* New Living
   Translation, 2nd ed. (Wheaton, IL: Tyndale, 2004), 2094.
4. "Q & A Library: A Cure for Crohn's Disease?," http://www.drweil.
   com/drw/u/id/QAA400137; "IBS Treatment and Management,"
   http://www.ibsliving.com/whatis_treatment.aspx; "How to Cure IBS
   Permanently," http://www.youtube.com/watch?v=eInvmxGhsko.

Chapter 20: Concluding Truths

1. http://www.livestrong.com/article/378552-what-happens-if-you-
   dont-eat-healthy-food/.

CONTACT INFORMATION

To order additional copies of this book, please visit
www.redemption-press.com.
Also available on Amazon.com and BarnesandNoble.com
Or by calling toll free 1 (888) 305-2967.